Common Core Progress

Mathematics

K

D1308030

Sadlier School

Common Core Progress
Mathematics

Cover: *Series Design:* Studio Montage;
Title design: Quarasan, Inc.

Photo Credits: *Cover:* Dreamstime.com/Tony Campbell: *top right;* Nano83: *top left;* Olinkau: *bottom left;* Photowitch: *bottom right.* Used under license from Shutterstock.com/ RoboLab: *background. Interior:* age fotostock/Japack: 9. Dreamstime.com/Viktor Gladkov: vi *top right;* Nano83: vi *center.* Getty images/Blend Images/Ariel Skelley: 8 *top;* Mark Bowden: 184 *top;* KidStock: 76 *top,* 128 top. Used under license from Shutterstock.com/elisekurenbina: vi *bottom left;* Eric Issellee: 185 *top;* FocusDzign: vi *top left;* Alina G: 185 *background;* Jana Guothova: 8 *bottom,* 76 *bottom,* 128 *bottom,* 184 *bottom,* 204 *bottom;* Hannamariah: 185 *center;* Ian 2010: vi *bottom right;* Piotr Krzeslak: 185 *bottom;* RoboLab: 1, vi *background.* SuperStock/Exactostock: 204 top.

Illustration Credits: Sarah Beise: 67-70, 148-150, 171-174, 187 middle and *bottom,* 235-242, 250. Used under license for Shutterstock.com/Matthew Cole: 10, 19 top and *bottom center,* 20, 21, 87-90. Dave Garbot: 27-34, 59-62, 106 *bottom,* 119-122, 135-138, 159-162, 187 *top,* 188-190, 199, 200, 231-234. Bob Holt: 8, 11-14, 23-26, 39-42, 47-54, 71-74, 92, 99-102, 123, 124, 126, 130, 132-134, 143-146, 156-158, 167-170, 191-194, 196-198, 201, 202, 254. Darren McKee: 35-38, 56-58, 93, 94, 140-142, 179, 180, 182. Bob Ostrom: 79-82, 91. Zina Saunders: 19 top *center* and *bottom.* Jackie Stafford: 15-18, 43-46, 63-66, 151-154, 164-166, 209, 210, 213, 214, 222.

For additional online resources, go to sadlierconnect.com.

Copyright © 2014 by William H. Sadlier, Inc. All rights reserved.

This publication, or any part thereof, may not be reproduced in any form, or by any means, including electronic, photographic, or mechanical, or by any sound recording system, or by any device for storage or retrieval of information, without the written permission of the publisher. Address inquiries to Permission Department, William H. Sadlier, Inc., 9 Pine Street, New York, NY 10005-4700.

S is a registered trademark of William H. Sadlier, Inc.

William H. Sadlier, Inc.
9 Pine Street
New York, NY 10005-4700

Printed in the United States of America.
ISBN: 978-1-4217-3150-6
1 2 3 4 5 6 7 8 9 WEBC 17 16 15 14

Common Core State Standards Copyright © 2010. National Governors Association Center for Best Practices and Council of Chief State School Officers. All rights reserved.

Contents

*Optional

continued on next page

continued on next page

Unit 4   Focus on Measurement and Data

Unit 5   Focus on Geometry

Welcome

You have an exciting year ahead of you. You will be learning about mathematics and the tools you will need to solve problems.

Did you know that you solve problems and use math every day? When you play sports, go shopping, cook, build something, or travel in a car, bus or train, you are using math.

Common Core Progress will help you improve your math skills. With it, you may even do better in school. That's why the book is called *Progress*.

Have a great year!

Progress Check

In this unit you will learn about Counting and Cardinality. The lessons in this unit cover all the Common Core Standards for Counting and Cardinality.

To practice your skills, go to sadlierconnect.com.

Before Unit 1	Can I ?	After Unit 1
☐	Count and model 0, 1, 2, 3, 4, 5, 6, 7, 8, 9, 10 **K.CC.4, K.CC.5, K.NBT.1**	☐
☐	Count and write 0, 1, 2, 3, 4, 5, 6, 7, 8, 9, 10 **K.CC.3, K.CC.5**	☐
☐	Match to compare **K.CC.6**	☐
☐	Count to compare **K.CC.5, K.CC.6**	☐
☐	Count to tell how many **K.CC.3, K.CC.5**	☐
☐	Compare numbers **K.CC.7**	☐
☐	Use ordinal numbers	☐

In this unit your child will:

- Count to tell the number of objects in a group, to 10.

- Model up to 10 objects.

- Read and write numbers to 10.

- Compare groups of objects and numbers, to 10.

Note: All of these learning goals for your child are based on the Grade K Common Core State Standards for Mathematics.

Ways to Help Your Child

You can count and use numbers as you interact with your child every day. For example, look for opportunities to count stairs, grapes, buttons on a jacket, or doors in a hallway. Let your child use counting to perform tasks such as setting the table for a meal. And, if your child enjoys picture books, the library stocks a variety of books that feature numbers to 10.

Your child begins the year counting to 10 and making the connection between number names, such as 4, and the quantity of an object. So, while counting objects to find *how many*, you may hear: "one, two, three, four, there are four balls."

Young children may not believe that all of the following images can show 4 objects, so groups are intentionally displayed in different arrangements for children to count.

Look for your kindergartner to write a number to represent a group of objects, as well as to use matching and counting strategies to compare groups and to discover that a number such as 8 is greater than 4.

Activity: Make a group of up to 10 objects that are alike and ask your child "how many" questions. With each try, vary the number of objects and how they are arranged (in a row, a circle, 3 rows of 3, or scattered). Notice whether your child understands that the last number name said tells the number of objects.

ONLINE

For more Home Connect activities, continue online at sadlierconnect.com

Focus on Counting and Cardinality

Essential Question:
How do you count?

Counting and Cardinality

●	1	one
● ●	2	two
● ● ●	3	three
● ● ● ●	4	four
● ● ● ● ●	5	five

2

4

5

3

Count each group of objects to find how many. Then draw a line to match the objects to the number you counted.

Count and Model 1 and 2

Learn about 1 and 2.

K.CC.4, K.CC.5

Guided Instruction **Count to tell how many.**

♥ Count to tell how many frogs.
🦋 Count to tell how many turtles.
🧸 Count the swans. Tell how many swans.
🦆 Count the fish. Tell how many fish.

1
one

2
two

Guided Instruction

♥ Count to tell how many leaves. There is one leaf. Look at the number **1** and the number name **one**.

🦋 Trace the **1** circle.

🐻 Count to tell how many flowers. There are two flowers. Look at the number **2** and the number name **two**.

🦆 Draw 2 circles.

♥

🦋

(1)   2   1   2

🧸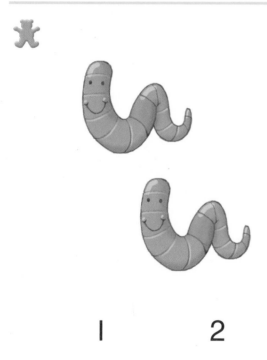

🦆

1   2   1   2

Guided Practice

♥ 🦋 🧸 🦆 Count the animals. Circle the number that tells how many.

Guided Practice

♥ 🦋 Count the number of objects in each group. Circle the group of 1 object. Draw an X on the group of 2 objects.

🧸 Draw 1 circle.

🦆 Draw 2 circles.

⭐ Omar counts the hearts. He says there is 1 heart. Is he correct? Explain why or why not.

Learn to write 1 and 2.

K.CC.3, K.CC.5

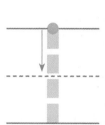

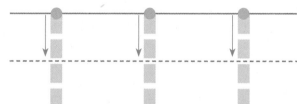

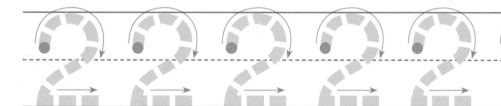

Guided Instruction **Write numbers to tell how many.**

♥ Count the guitars. There is one guitar. Trace the number 1. Trace the other 1s.

🦋 Count the drums. There are two drums. Trace the number 2. Trace the other 2s.

♥

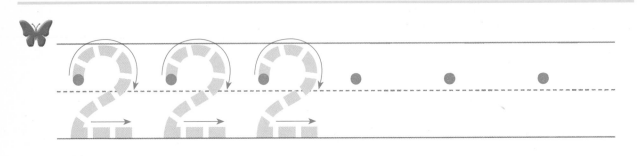

🐻

🦆

Guided Instruction

♥ Trace the 1s. Start at each blue dot to write more 1s.

🦋 Trace the 2s. Start at each blue dot to write more 2s.

🐻 🦆 Count how many instruments. Write the number that tells how many.

_____

- - - - - - - - - -

_____

_____

- - - - - - - - - -

_____

_____

- - - - - - - - - -

_____

_____

- - - - - - - - - -

_____

_____

- - - - - - - - - -

_____

_____

- - - - - - - - - -

_____

Guided Practice

 Count how many instruments. Write the number that tells how many.

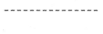

 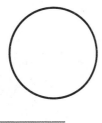   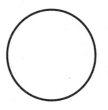

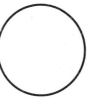

MP4

Guided Practice

♥ 🦋 🧸 🦆 Count how many. Write the number that tells how many.

⭐ Color one circle red. Color two circles blue. Write the number that tells how many red circles there are. Write the number that tells how many blue circles there are.

18   Unit 1 ■ Focus on Counting and Cardinality

Lesson 3

Count and Model
3 and 4

Learn about
3 and 4.

K.CC.4, K.CC.5

Guided Instruction **Count to tell how many.**

Count the horses. Tell how many horses.
Count the stacks of hay. Tell how many stacks of hay.
Count the cows. Tell how many cows.
Count the pails of milk. Tell how many pails of milk.

3
three

4
four

Guided Instruction

♥ Count to tell how many ducks. There are three ducks. Look at the number **3** and the number name **three**.

W Draw 3 circles.

🐻 Count to tell how many chickens. There are four chickens. Look at the number **4** and the number name **four**.

🦆 Draw 4 circles.

3   4

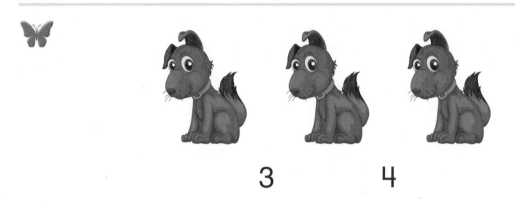

3   4

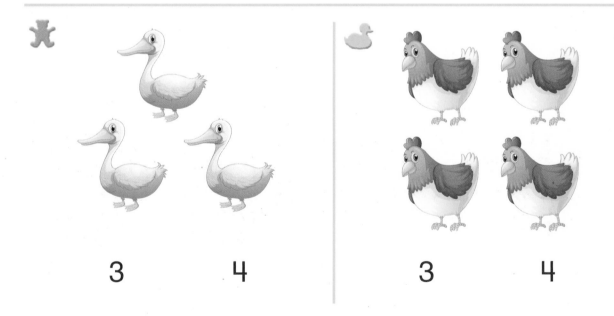

3   4   3   4

Guided Practice

♥ 🦋 🧸 🦆 Count the animals. Circle the number that tells how many.

MP2

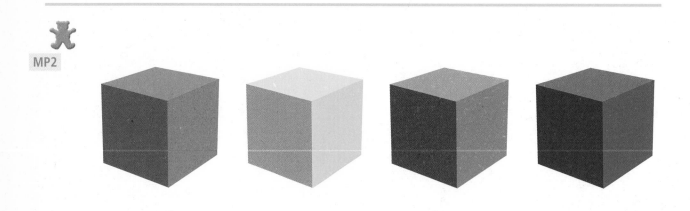

Guided Practice

 Draw 3 circles.

 Draw 4 circles.

Marie counts the blocks starting with the red one. Darrell counts the blocks starting from the purple one. Who will get the correct answer? Explain.

Lesson 4

Count and Write 3 and 4

Learn to write 3 and 4.

K.CC.3, K.CC.5

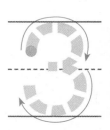

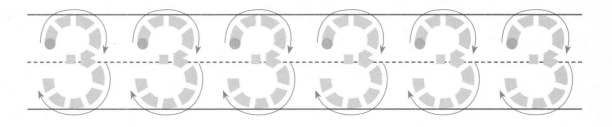

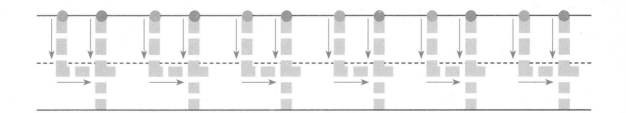

Guided Instruction Write numbers to tell how many.

 Count the suns. There are three suns. Trace the number 3. Trace the other 3s.

 Count the umbrellas. There are four umbrellas. Trace the number 4.
Trace the other 4s.

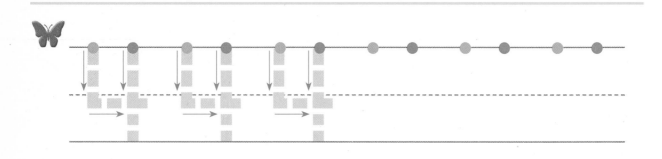

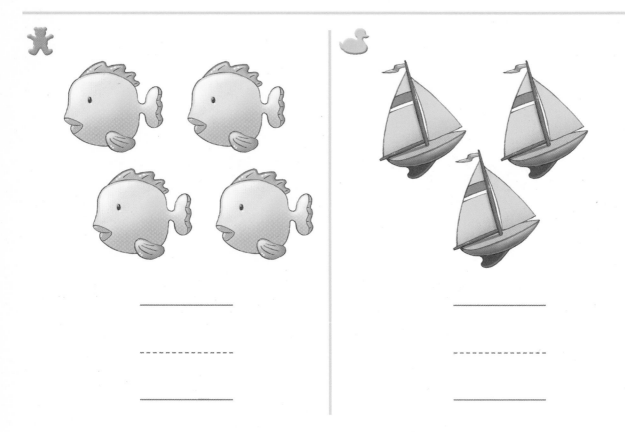

Guided Instruction

♥ Trace the 3s. Start at each blue dot to write more 3s.
🦋 Trace the 4s. Start at each blue dot to write more 4s.
🧸 Count the fish. Write the number that tells how many.
🦆 Count the sailboats. Write the number that tells how many.

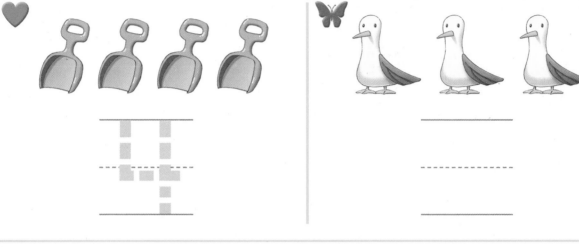

Guided Practice

♥ 🦋 🧩 🦆 ⭐ 🐢 Count how many. Write the number that tells how many.

♥

_____

- - - - - - - - - -

_____

🦋

_____

- - - - - - - - - -

_____

🧸

_____

- - - - - - - - - -

_____

🦆

_____

- - - - - - - - - -

_____

⭐

MP1

_____   _____   _____   _____

- - - - - -   - - - - - -   - - - - - -   - - - - - -

_____   _____   _____   _____

Guided Practice

♥ 🦋 🧸 🦆 Count how many. Write the number that tells how many.

⭐ Dylan writes the numbers 1 to 4. He circles the number that has no straight lines. Write to show what is on Dylan's paper.

Count and Model 0 and 5

Learn about 0 and 5.

K.CC.4, K.CC.5

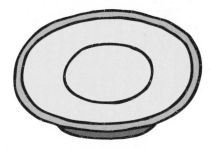

Guided Instruction **Count to tell how many.**

♥ Tell how many apples are in the bowl.
🦋 Count to tell how many strawberries.
🐻 Tell how many muffins are on the plate.
🦆 Count the apples. Tell how many apples.

5
five

0
zero

Guided Instruction

♥ Count to tell how many bananas. There are five bananas. Look at the number **5** and the number name **five**.
🦋 Draw 5 circles.

🧸 Tell how many plates are on the table. There are no plates. Look at the number **0** and the number name **zero**.
🦆 Draw 0 circles.

0   5

0   5

0   5

0   5

Guided Practice

♥ 🦋 🧸 🦆 Count the berries on each plate. Circle the number that
tells how many.

 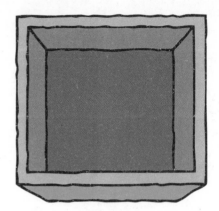

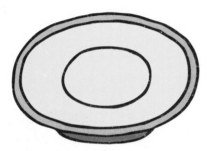 

MP4

Guided Practice

💜 Count the number of oranges in each crate.
Circle the crate with 0 oranges. Draw an X on
the crate with 5 oranges.

🦋 Count the number of pears on each plate. Circle the
plate with 0 pears. Draw an X on the plate with 5 pears.

🐻 Julian draws a house with 5 windows and 0 doors.
Draw a house like the one Julian could have drawn.

Learn to write 0 and 5.

K.CC.3, K.CC.5

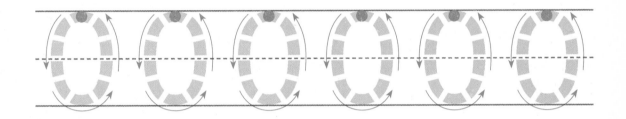

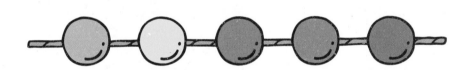

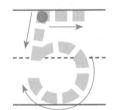

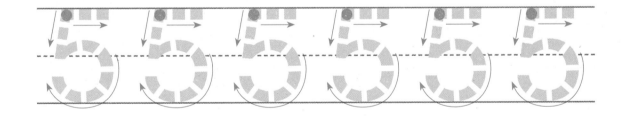

Guided Instruction **Write numbers to tell how many.**

♥ Tell how many beads are on the string. There are zero beads. Trace the number 0. Trace the other 0s.

🦋 Count the beads. There are five beads. Trace the number 5. Trace the other 5s.

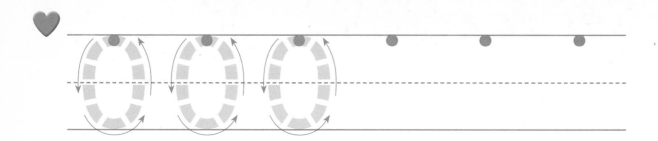

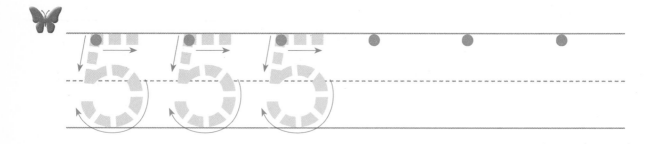

Guided Instruction

♥ Trace the 0s. Start at each blue dot to write more 0s.

🦋 Trace the 5s. Start at each blue dot to write more 5s.

🧸 🦆 Count how many eggs are in the nest. Write the number that tells how many.

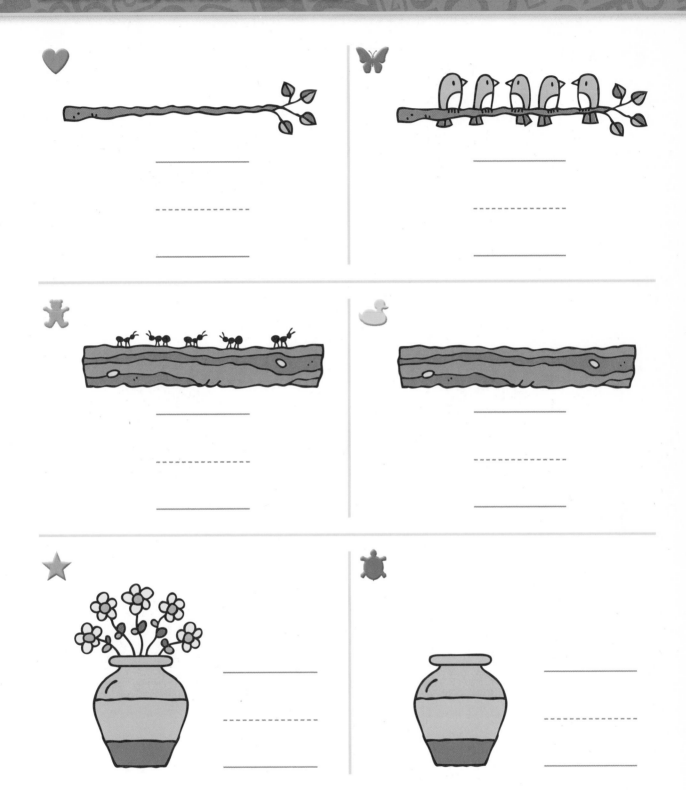

Guided Practice

♥ 🦋 Count how many birds are on the branch. Write the number that tells how many.

🧸 🦆 Count how many ants are on the log. Write the number that tells how many.

⭐ 🐢 Count how many flowers are in the vase. Write the number that tells how many.

_____

- - - - - - - - - - -

_____

_____

- - - - - - - - - - -

_____

_____

- - - - - - - - - - -

_____

MP1

Guided Practice

 Count how many books are on the shelf. Write the number that tells how many.

 Count how many crayons are in the box. Write the number that tells how many.

Use these clues to find the mystery number.
Clue 1: One is the next counting number after the mystery number. Clue 2: The number means none. Write the mystery number.

Match to Compare

equal to

more than

fewer than

Guided Instruction **Match to compare objects.**

Introduce the phrases **equal to, more than,** and **fewer than**.

 Trace the lines to match the animals to the objects. Tell if the number
of animals is more than, fewer than, or equal to the number of objects.

Guided Instruction

💜 Trace the lines to match the yellow apples to the plates. Draw a circle around the apples and plates if the number of yellow apples is equal to the number of plates.

🦋 Trace the lines to match the red apples to the plates. Circle the group with more objects.

🧸 Trace and draw lines to match the green apples to the plates. Circle the group with fewer objects.

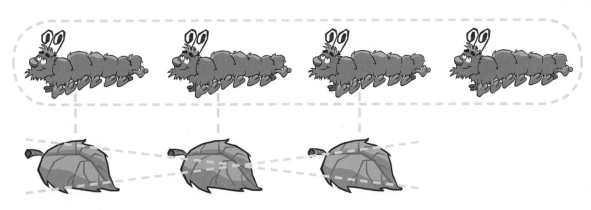

Guided Practice

♥ Trace the lines to match the caterpillars to the leaves. Trace the circle around the group with more objects. Trace the X on the group with fewer objects.

🦋 Draw lines to match the ladybug to the leaves. Circle the group with more objects. Draw an X on the group with fewer objects.

🧸 Draw lines to match the butterflies to the leaves. Draw a circle around the butterflies and leaves if the number of butterflies is equal to the number of leaves.

Unit 1 ■ Focus on Counting and Cardinality **37**

MP6

Guided Practice

♥ ✖ Draw lines to match the objects. Circle the group that has more objects.
Draw an X on the group that has fewer objects.

🧸 Draw a group of suns below the umbrellas. Draw lines to match the objects.
Tell if the number of umbrellas is more than, fewer than, or equal to the
number of suns you drew.

Count and Model 6 and 7

Learn about 6 and 7.

K.CC.4, K.CC.5

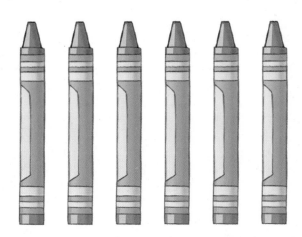

Guided Instruction **Count to tell how many.**

♥ Count the crayons. Tell how many crayons. Color one square for each crayon.

🦋 Count the buttons. Tell how many buttons. Color one square for each button.

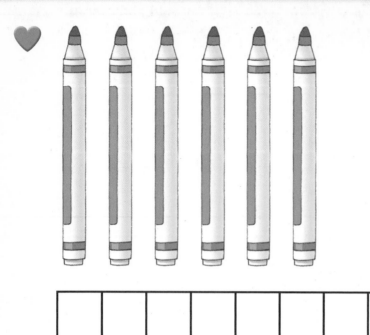

6
six

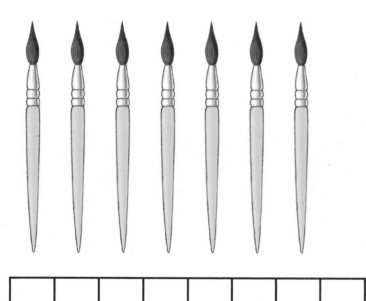

7
seven

Guided Instruction

♥ Count to tell how many markers. There are six markers. Look at the number **6** and the number name **six**. Color one square for each marker.

🦋 Count to tell the number of paint brushes. There are seven paintbrushes. Look at the number **7** and the number name **seven**. Color one square for each paint brush.

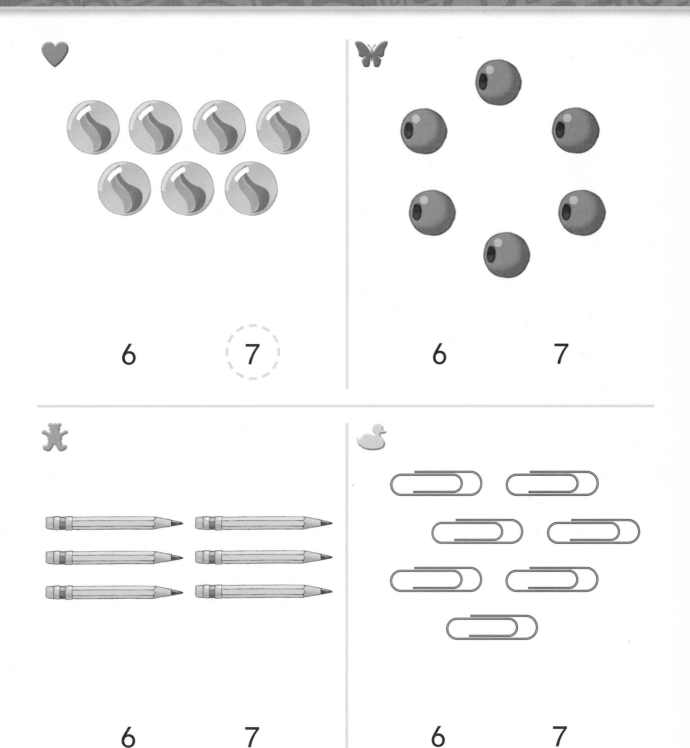

Guided Practice

♥ 🦋 🧸 🦆 Count the objects. Circle the number that tells how many.

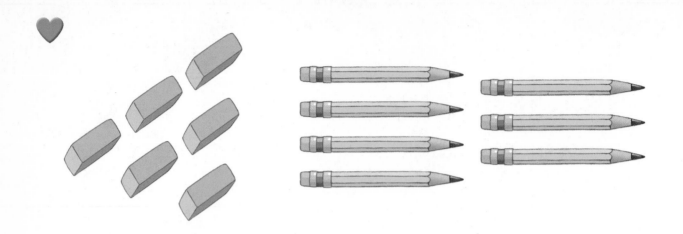

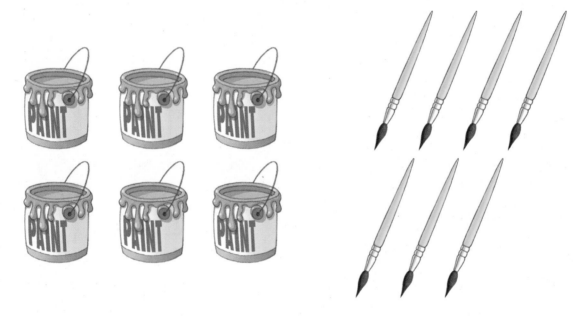

MP1

Guided Practice

 🦋 Count the number of objects in each group. Circle the group with 6 objects.
Draw an X on the group with 7 objects.

🧸 Kevin counts to 6 and then counts one more number. Draw circles to show
what Kevin's number means.

Count and Write
6 and 7

Learn to write 6 and 7.

K.CC.3, K.CC.5

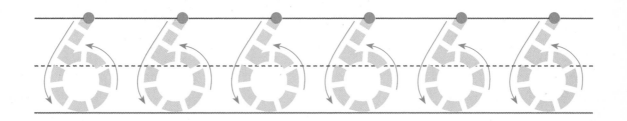

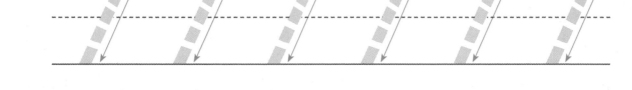

Guided Instruction **Write numbers to tell how many.**

♥ Count how many blocks. There are six blocks.
Trace the number 6. Trace the other 6s.

🦋 Count how many robots. There are seven robots.
Trace the number 7. Trace the other 7s.

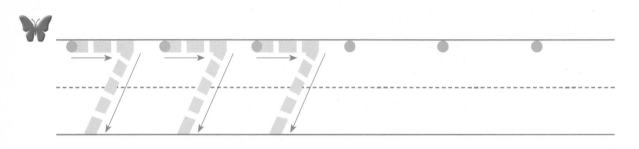

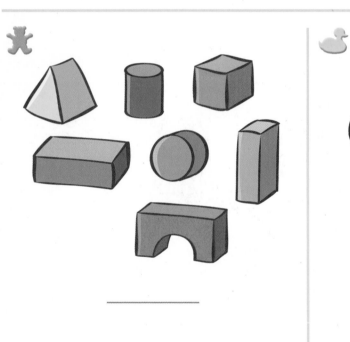

_____

- - - - - - - - - - -

_____

_____

- - - - - - - - - - -

_____

Guided Instruction

♥ Trace the 6s. Start at each blue dot to write more 6s.

🦋 Trace the 7s. Start at each blue dot to write more 7s.

🧸 🦆 Count how many objects. Write the number that tells how many.

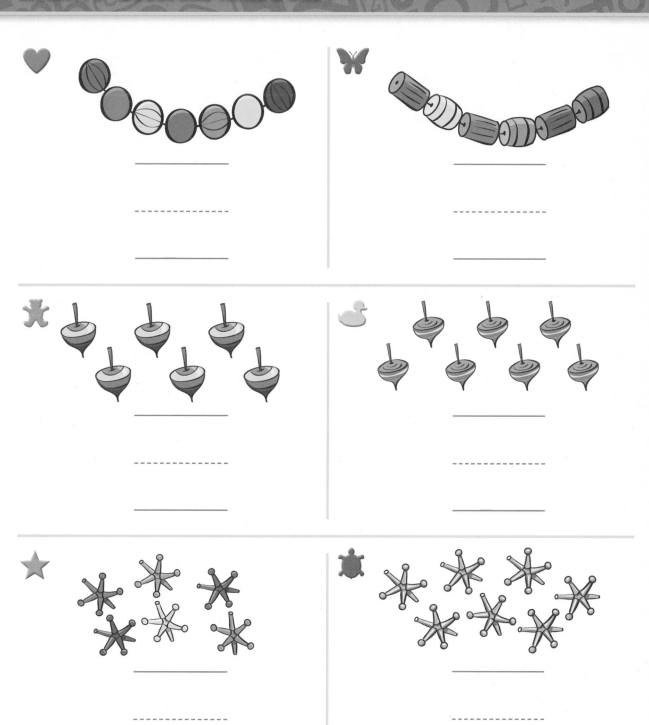

Guided Practice

♥ 🦋 🧸 🦆 ⭐ 🐢 Count how many. Write the number that tells how many.

_____

- - - - - - - - - - - - - - - -

_____

_____

- - - - - - - - - - - - - - - -

_____

_____

- - - - - - - - - - - - - - - -

_____

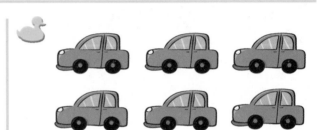

_____

- - - - - - - - - - - - - - - -

_____

MP2

_____

- - - - - - - - - - - - - - - -

_____

Guided Practice

Count how many. Write the number that tells how many.

Lauren tries to count the robots. She keeps losing her count.
Tell at least 2 things she can do to help her count correctly.
Then count and write how many.

Count and Model 8, 9, and 10

Learn about 8, 9, and 10.

K.CC.4, K.CC.5

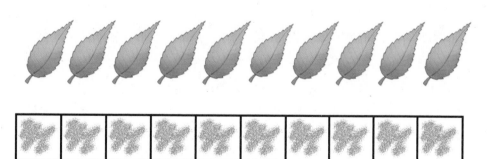

Guided Instruction **Count to tell how many.**

Count the acorns. Tell how many. Color one square for each acorn.

Count the flowers. Tell how many. Color one square for each flower.

Count the leaves. Tell how many. Color one square for each leaf.

8
eight

9
nine

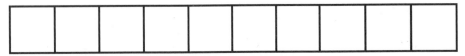

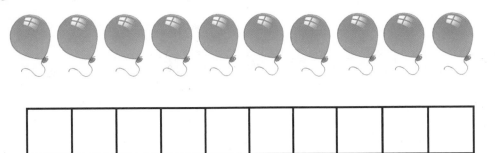

10
ten

Guided Instruction

♥ Count to tell how many blue balloons. There are eight blue balloons. Look at the number **8** and the number name **eight**. Color one square for each blue balloon.

🦋 Count to tell the number of red balloons. There are nine red balloons. Look at the number **9** and the number name **nine**. Color one square for each red balloon.

🧸 Count to tell the number of green balloons. There are ten green balloons. Look at the number **10** and the number name **ten**. Color one square for each green balloon.

♥ 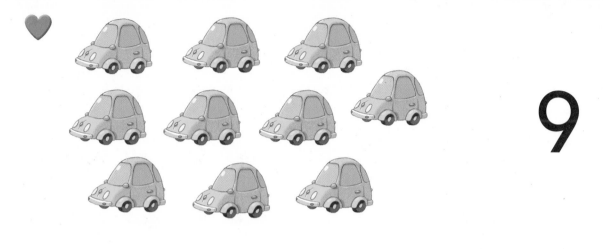 9

🦋 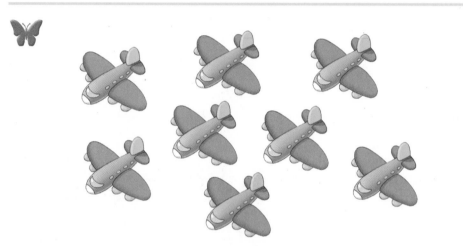 10

🧸 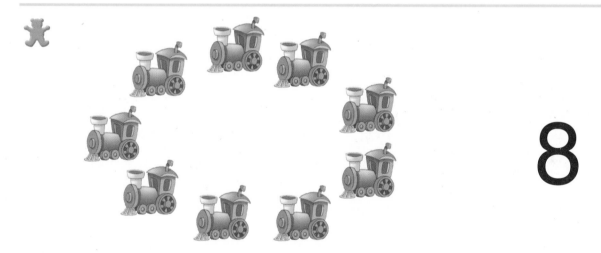 8

Guided Practice

♥ 🦋 🧸 Count the objects. Draw a line to the number that tells how many.

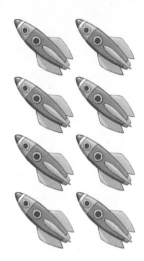

8   9   10   8   9   10

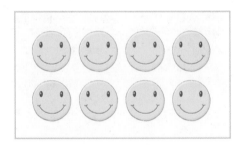   

MP8   8

9

10

Guided Practice

♥ 🦋 Count the objects. Circle the number that tells how many.

🐻 Circle the sticker page that has 10 stickers.

🦆 The marbles are in groups of 8, 9, and 10. Start at 8. As you move from one group to the next, tell how the new group is different.

Count and Write 8, 9, and 10

Learn to write 8, 9, and 10.

K.CC.3, K.CC.5

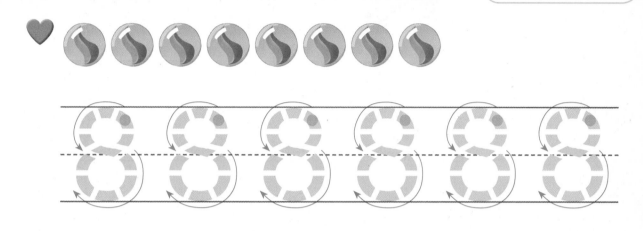

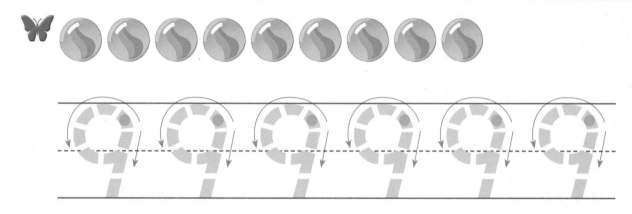

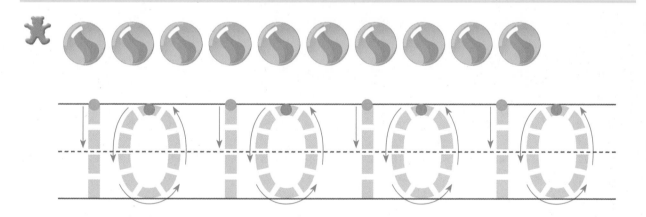

Guided Instruction **Write numbers to tell how many.**

♥ Count to tell how many marbles. There are eight marbles.
Trace the number 8s.

🦋 Count to tell how many marbles. There are nine marbles.
Trace the number 9s.

🧸 Count to tell how many marbles. There are ten marbles.
Trace the number 10s.

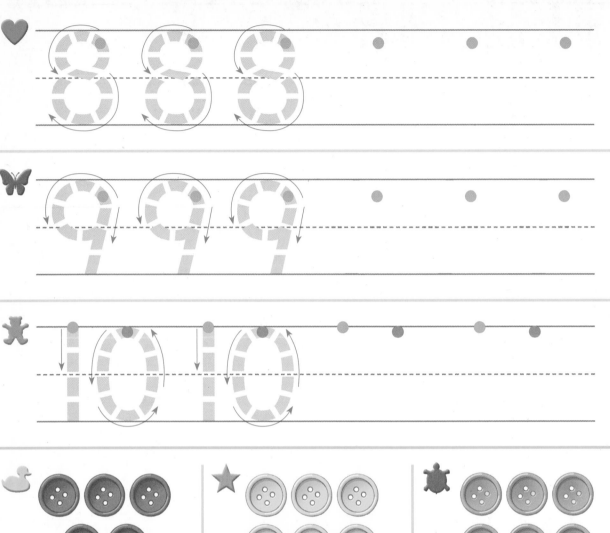

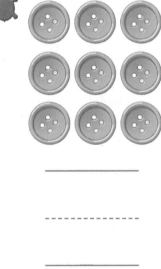

Guided Instruction

♥ Trace the 8s. Start at each blue dot to write more 8s.
🦋 Trace the 9s. Start at each blue dot to write more 9s.
🧸 Trace the 10s. Start at each blue dot to write more 10s.
🦆★🐢 Count how many buttons. Write the number that tells how many.

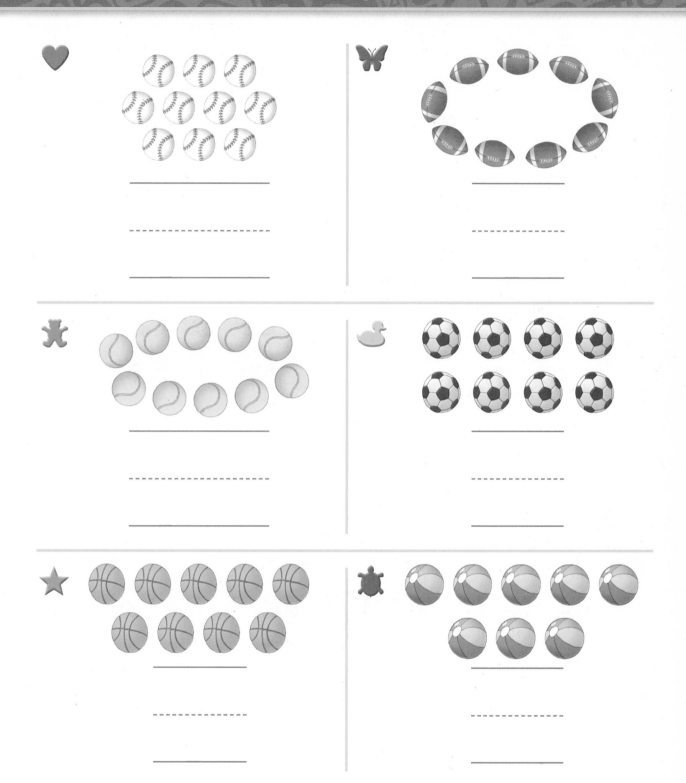

Guided Practice

♥ 🦋 🐻 🦆 ⭐ 🐢 Count how many. Write the number that tells how many.

♥

_____
- - - - - - - - - - - - - - - -
_____

🦋

_____
- - - - - - - - - - - - - - - -
_____

🐻

_____
- - - - - - - - - - - - - - - -
_____

🦆

_____
- - - - - - - - - - - - - - - -
_____

⭐

_____
- - - - - - - - - - - - - - - -
_____

_____
- - - - - - - - - - - - - - - -
_____

_____
- - - - - - - - - - - - - - - -
_____

Guided Practice

♥ 🦋 🐻 🦆 Count how many. Write the number that tells how many.
⭐ Count the dots on each side of the domino. Write how many dots are on each side. Count how many dots in all are on the domino. Write that number below the domino.

12 Count to Compare

2 is equal to 2

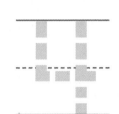
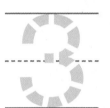

4 is greater than 3

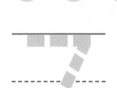

6 is less than 7

Guided Instruction **Count to compare.** Introduce the phrases **equal to**, **greater than**, and **less than**.

💜 Count the yellow counters. Count the red counters. Trace the numbers that tell how many of each color counter. Compare the numbers. They are the same. 2 is equal to 2.

🦋 Count the yellow counters. Count the red counters. Trace the numbers that tell how many of each color counter. Compare the numbers. 4 is greater than 3.

🧸 Count the yellow counters. Count the red counters. Trace the numbers that tell how many of each color counter. Compare the numbers. 6 is less than 7.

♥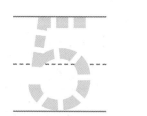

5   5

🦋

🧸

Guided Instruction

♥ Count the hats in each group. Trace the numbers that tell how many in each group.
Compare the numbers. Draw a circle around the numbers if they are equal.

🦋 Count the hats in each group. Write the number that tells how many in each group.
Draw a circle around the number that is greater.

🧸 Count the hats in each group. Write how many in each group.
Draw a circle around the number that is less.

56   **Unit 1** ■ Focus on Counting and Cardinality

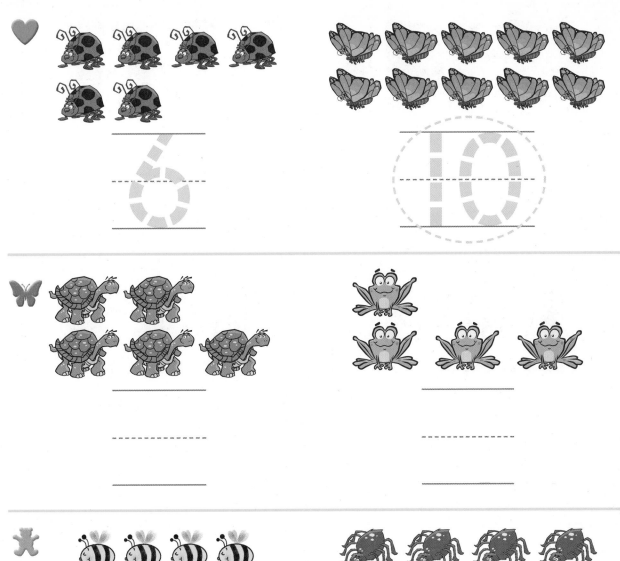

Guided Practice

♥ Count the ladybugs. Trace the number that tells how many. Count the butterflies.
Trace the number that tells how many. Circle the number that is greater.

🦋 Count the turtles. Write the number that tells how many. Count the frogs.
Write the number that tells how many. Circle the number that is less.

🧸 Count the bees. Write the number that tells how many. Count the spiders.
Write the number that tells how many. Circle the number that is greater.

Lesson 12 **Count to Compare**

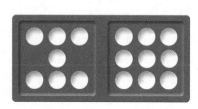

MP2

Guided Practice

Count the dots on each side of the domino. Write how many. Circle the greater number.

Draw dots on one wing of the ladybug. Draw an equal number of dots on the other wing. Write how many on each wing.

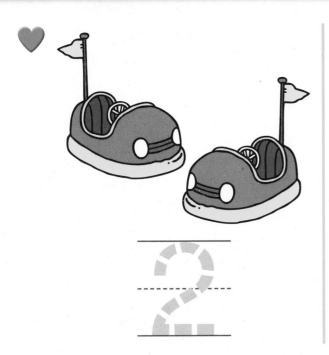

2

11

9

Guided Instruction Count to tell how many.

♥ Count the bumper cars. Trace the number that tells how many.
🦋 🧸 Count the balloons. Trace the number that tells how many.
🦆 Count the milk bottles. Write the number that tells how many.

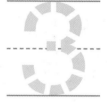

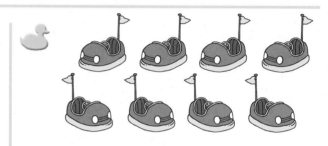

Guided Instruction

♥ 🦋 Count each roller coaster car. Trace the number that tells how many.

🧸 🦆 ⭐ 🐢 Count each object. Write the number that tells how many.

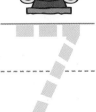

Guided Practice

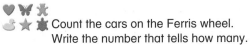
Count the cars on the Ferris wheel.
Write the number that tells how many.

ONE ONE ONE ONE ONE ONE ONE ONE ONE ONE

_____

- - - - - - - - - - - - - - -

_____

_____

- - - - - - - - - -

_____

_____

- - - - - - - - - -

_____

MP1

_____

- - - - - - - - - -

_____

Guided Practice

♥ Count the tickets. Write the number that tells how many.
🦋 Count the slides. Write the number that tells how many.
🧸 Count the ducks. Write the number that tells how many.
🦆 Count the fishbowls. Draw one more. Now count all the bowls.
Write the number that tells how many bowls there are now.

Compare Numbers

Learn to compare numbers.

K.CC.7

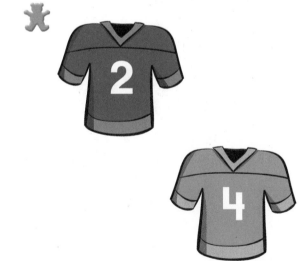

Guided Instruction   Compare two numbers.

Look at the numbers on the jerseys at the top of the page.
They are in order from 1 to 10.
♥ 🦋 Compare the numbers. Trace the circle around the greater number.
🧸 🦆 Compare the numbers. Circle the number that is less.

Lesson 14 Compare Numbers

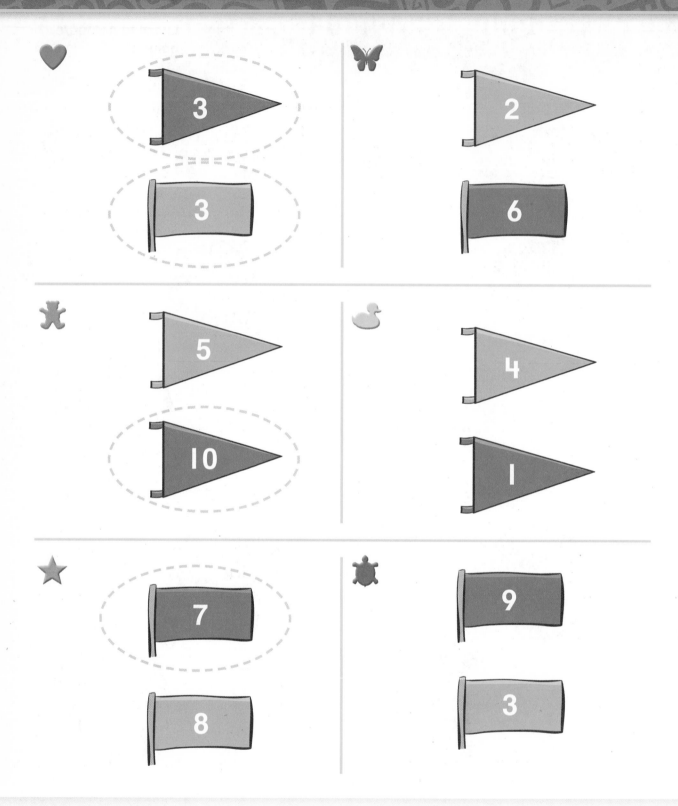

Guided Instruction

♥ 🦋 Compare the numbers. Trace/Draw a circle around both numbers if they are equal.

🧸 🦆 Compare the numbers. Trace/Draw a circle around the greater number.

⭐ 🐢 Compare the numbers. Trace/Draw a circle around the number that is less.

64 Unit 1 ■ Focus on Counting and Cardinality

Lesson 14 Compare Numbers

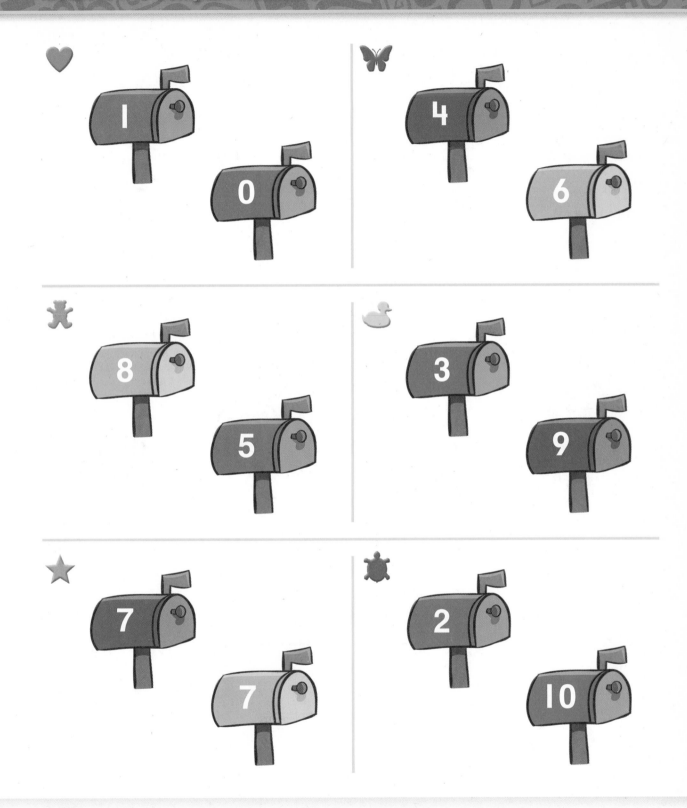

Guided Practice

♥ 🦋 Compare the numbers. Circle the greater number.

🧸 🦆 Compare the numbers. Circle the number that is less.

⭐ 🐢 Compare the numbers. Draw a circle around both numbers if they are equal.

♥

7

5

🦋

4

2

🧸

6

3

🦆

8

9

⭐
MP1
MP3

Kobe's Number   Ally's Number

_____   _____

- - - - - - - - - - -   - - - - - - - - - - -

_____   _____

Guided Practice

♥ 🦋 🧸 🦆 Compare the numbers. Circle the greater number. Draw an X on the number that is less.

⭐ Kobe's number is the number of legs a dog has. Ally's number is the next counting number after 3. Write their numbers. Ally says her number is less than Kobe's number. Is she correct? Explain why or why not.

15 Ordinal Numbers

first second third fourth fifth sixth seventh eighth ninth tenth

Guided Instruction Use ordinal numbers to tell positions.

Introduce the ordinal numbers first through tenth.

♥ Touch each bee as you read the words.

🦋 Trace the circle around the first bird. Trace the X on the fifth bird.

🐻 Trace the circle around the third duckling. Trace the X on the seventh duckling.

🦆 Trace the circle around the tenth worm. Trace the X on the sixth worm.

⭐ Draw a circle around the ninth butterfly. Draw an X on the second butterfly.

Guided Instruction

♥ Trace the circle around the ninth duckling. Draw an X on the third duckling.

🦋 Trace the circle around the fourth grasshopper. Draw an X on the eighth grasshopper.

🐻 Trace the circle around the second bee. Draw an X on the sixth bee.

🦆 Circle the seventh bird. Draw an X on the fifth bird.

⭐ Circle the tenth worm. Draw an X on the first worm.

68 Unit 1 ■ Focus on Counting and Cardinality

Guided Practice

♥ Draw a circle around the third child. Draw an X on the ninth child.
🦋 Draw a circle around the seventh child. Draw an X on the fifth child.
🧸 Draw a circle around the second bunny. Draw an X on the first bunny.
🦆 Draw a circle around the fourth puppy. Draw an X on the eighth puppy.

MP3

Guided Practice

♥ Circle the third snail. Draw an X on the fifth snail.

🦋 Circle the eighth squirrel. Draw an X on the second squirrel.

🧸 Circle the ninth frog. Draw an X on the first frog.

🦆 Circle the sixth ant. Draw an X on the tenth ant.

⭐ Ethan says the child with the tambourine is eighth. Zoey says the child with the tambourine is third. Who is correct? Explain.

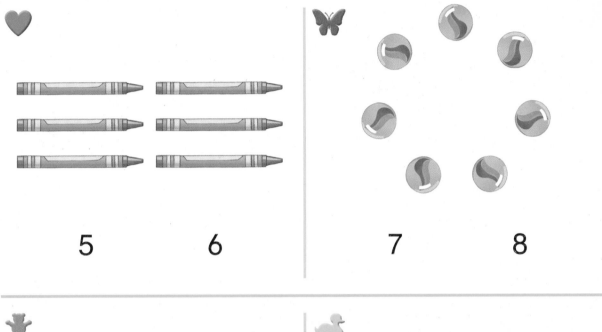

♥

5   6

🦋

7   8

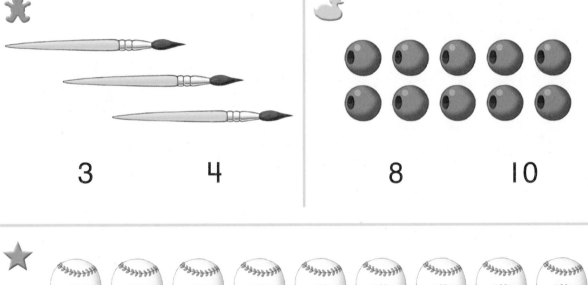

🐻

3   4

🦆

8   10

⭐

7   9

♥ 🦋 🐻 🦆 ⭐ Count the objects. Circle the number that tells how many.

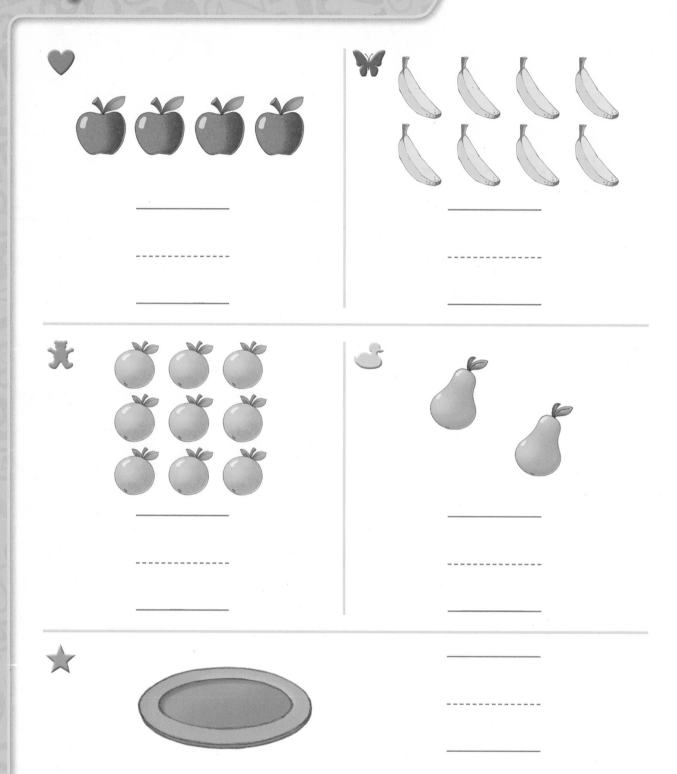

♥ 🦋 🐻 🦆 Count the pieces of fruit. Write how many.
⭐ Write how many pieces of fruit are on the plate.

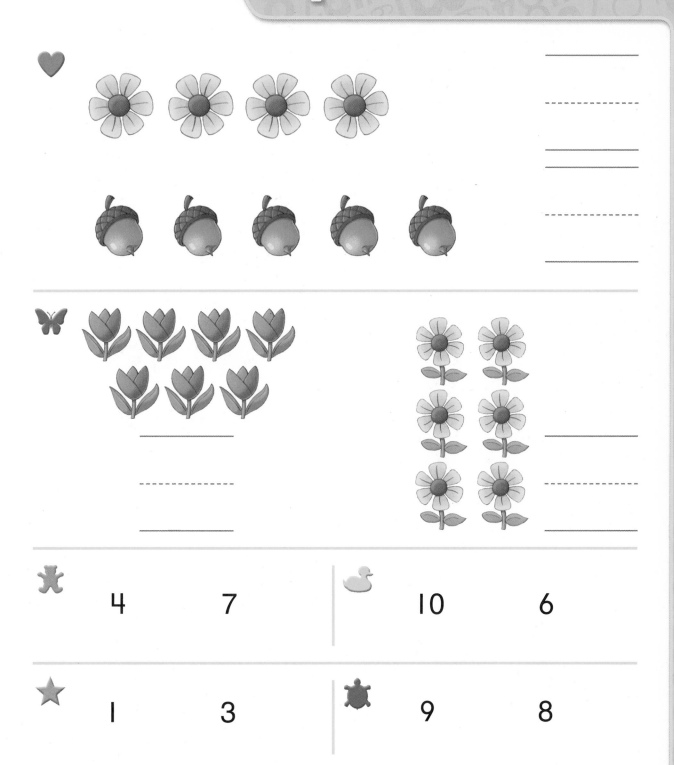

♥   4   7   🦆   10   6

⭐   1   3   🐢   9   8

♥ Count and write how many in each group. Draw lines to compare
the groups. Circle the number that is less.

🦋 Count and write how many in each group. Compare the numbers.
Circle the number that is greater.

🧸🦆 Compare the numbers. Circle the number that is greater.

⭐🐢 Compare the numbers. Circle the number that is less.

Unit 1 ■ Focus on Counting and Cardinality   **73**

first

first

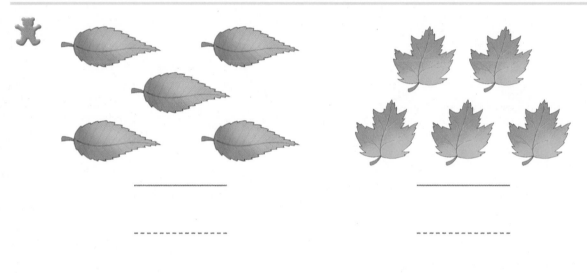

_____

- - - - - - - - - - - - - - -   - - - - - - - - - - - - - - -

_____   _____

MP3

💜 Circle the second butterfly. Underline the fifth butterfly.
🦋 Circle the sixth bird. Underline the ninth bird.
🧸 Count and write how many in each group. Tell if the number of objects in the first group
 is greater than, less than, or equal to the number of objects in the second group.
🦆 Ava says there is a greater number of fish than hearts. Tell if she is correct.
 Tell how you know.

Progress Check

In this unit you will learn about Operations and Algebraic Thinking. The lessons in this unit cover all the Common Core Standards for Operations and Algebraic Thinking.

To practice your skills, go to sadlierconnect.com.

Before Unit 2	Can I ?	After Unit 2
☐	Use models to show addition K.OA.1	☐
☐	Solve problems with addition K.OA.2	☐
☐	Use models to show subtraction K.OA.1	☐
☐	Solve problems with subtraction K.OA.2	☐
☐	Show numbers to 10 in more than one way K.OA.3	☐
☐	Find pairs of numbers that make 10 K.OA.4	☐
☐	Add to find sums to 5 K.OA.5	☐
☐	Subtract from 5 or less K.OA.5	☐

In this unit your child will:

- Add to find how many in all.

- Subtract to find how many are left.

- Solve addition and subtraction word problems.

- Make a 10 from a starting number.

- Break apart numbers to 10.

- Fluently add and subtract within 5.

Note: All of these learning goals for your child are based on the Grade K Common Core State Standards for Mathematics.

Ways to Help Your Child

Your child may feel most comfortable with one addition or subtraction method, for example modeling with objects, using fingers to act out, drawing a picture, or making sounds or movements to solve. Support that approach but also encourage your child to use the other methods as you point out real-world problem situations, such as: "You made 3 goals on Saturday and 2 on Sunday. How many goals did you make this weekend?" or "I bought 4 apples but then you ate 1. I wonder how many apples are left."

Your child will begin to explore addition and subtraction. Over time there will be an understanding that addition involves putting together and adding to, while subtraction is breaking apart and taking from. Your child may use various methods such as their fingers, objects, and drawings to model or act out situations and word problems.

It is important that children realize that numbers can be decomposed or broken apart in more than one way. For example:

$$4 = 3 + 1$$

$$4 = 2 + 2$$

Being able to add and subtract easily within 5 builds a foundation for mastery of all addition and subtraction facts in Grade 1.

Activity: Play a card game, "Make 10." Draw dot cards or use playing cards to create two cards for each number 1 through 9. Shuffle the cards and place them face up. Choose one card and display it. Your child looks for a card that together with the displayed card makes the number 10, such as 9 and 1. Play together until all cards are matched. You can play again, this time beginning with all cards face down.

ONLINE
For more Home Connect activities, continue online at sadlierconnect.com

Focus on Operations and Algebraic Thinking

Essential Question:
How do you add and subtract?

Ways to Make 4 and 5

4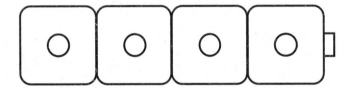

5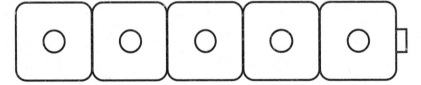

♥ Make a name for 4. Color with red and blue crayons.
🦋 🧸 Make names for 5. Color with red and blue crayons.

16   Put Together to Add

Learn to put groups together.

K.OA.1

2 and **1** in all

 and   in all

 and   in all

Guided Instruction   **Put together to find how many in all.**

♥ Read the numbers that tell how many children in each group. Trace the number that tells how many in all when you put the groups together.

🦋 🧸 Trace the numbers that tell how many children in each group. Trace the number that tells how many in all when you put the groups together.

 and  in all

 and _____ in all

_____ and _____ _____ in all

Guided Instruction

♥ Trace the numbers that tell how many cars in each group. Trace the number that tells how many cars in all when you put the groups together.

🦋 Trace the number that tells how many red crayons. Trace the number that tells how many green crayons. Write the number that tells how many crayons in all.

🧸 Write the numbers that tell how many flowers are in each group. Write the number that tells how many flowers in all.

Lesson 16 Put Together to Add

3 and 2 5 in all

_____ and _____ _____ in all

_____ and _____ _____ in all

Guided Practice

♥ Trace the numbers that tell how many birds in each group. Trace the number that tells how many birds in all when you put the groups together.

🦋 Write the numbers that tell how many ducks in each group. Write the number that tells how many ducks in all.

🧸 Write the numbers that tell how many kittens in each group. Write the number that tells how many kittens in all.

_____

_____ and _____ _____ in all

_____

_____ and _____ _____ in all

MP7

2 and 3 _____ in all

Guided Practice

 Write the numbers that tell how many in each group. Write the number that tells how many in all.

Draw a picture to show the number in each group. Write the number that tells how many in all when you put the groups together.

17 Add to Find How Many

Learn to add to find how many in all.

K.OA.1

 and =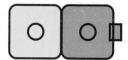

$$1 + 1 = 2$$

plus   equals

 +  =

$$1 + 2 = 3$$

plus   equals

$$3 + 1 = \underline{\hspace{1cm}}$$

plus   equals

Guided Instruction Add to find how many in all.

 Introduce the **plus** and **equal** signs. Look at each group of cubes. Read the numbers that tell how many yellow cubes and how many red cubes. Add to find how many in all. 1 plus 1 equals 2. Trace the number that tells how many cubes in all.

 Trace the numbers that tell how many in each group. Trace the number that tells how many in all.

 Trace the numbers that tell how many in each group. Write the number that tells how many in all.

Unit 2 ■ Focus on Operations and Algebraic Thinking **83**

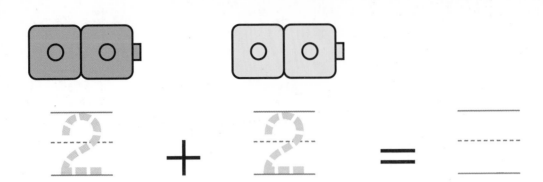

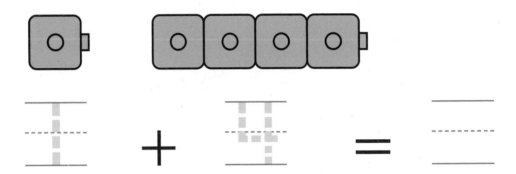

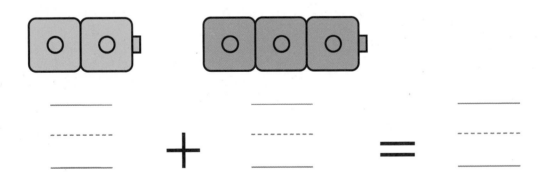

Guided Instruction

♥ 🦋 Trace the numbers that tell how many in each group. Add the numbers in each group to find how many in all. Write the number that tells how many in all.

🧸 Write the numbers that tell how many in each group. Write the number that tells how many in all.

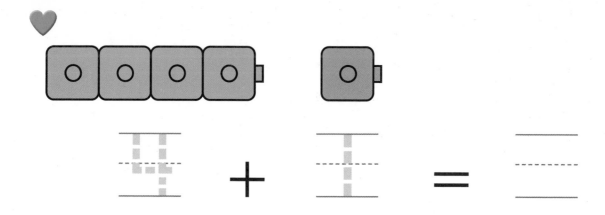

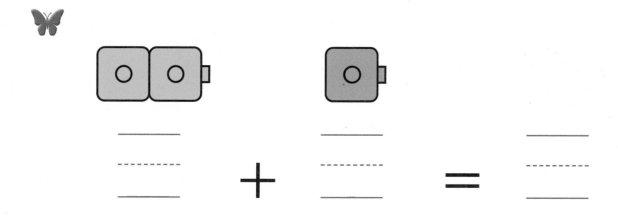

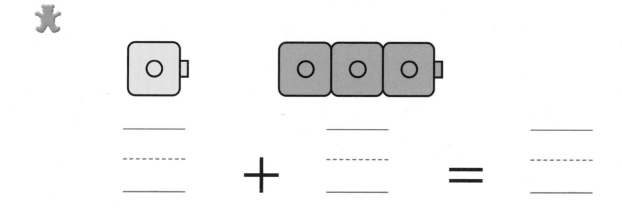

Guided Practice

♥ Trace the numbers that tell how many in each group. Add the numbers and trace the number that tells how many in all.

🦋 🐻 Write the numbers that tell how many in each group. Write the number that tells how many in all.

♥

_____

\- \- \- \- \-   +   \- \- \- \- \-   =   \- \- \- \- \-

_____

🦋

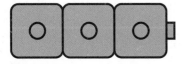

_____

\- \- \- \- \-   +   \- \- \- \- \-   =   \- \- \- \- \-

_____

🧸

MP4

1   +   4   =   _____

Guided Practice

♥🦋 Write the numbers that tell how many in each group. Add to find how many in all. Write the number that tells how many in all.

🧸 Draw a picture to show how many in each group. Then write the number that tells how many in all.

1 .

4 more  join in.

How many now?

$1 + 4 = 5$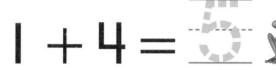

3 .

4 more  join in.

How many 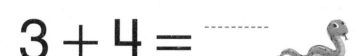 now?

$3 + 4 = \underline{}$

Guided Instruction **Solve problems with addition.**

Introduce the term **addition sentence**.

♥🦋 Read the problem. Trace the circles that match the numbers in the problem.
Add the numbers. Trace/write the number that tells how many there are now.
Read the addition sentence.

3 .

Kim picks 1 more 🍓.

How many 🍓 now?

3 + 1 = ___ 🍓

4 🍐.

Dan picks 4 more 🍐.

How many 🍐 in all?

4 + 4 = ___ 🍐

Guided Instruction

 Read the problem. Trace the circles that match the numbers in the problem. Add the numbers. Trace the number that tells how many there are now. Read the addition sentence.

 Read the problem. Draw a picture to match the problem. Write the number that tells how many there are in all. Read the addition sentence.

3 .

5 more join in.

How many now?

$3 + 5 = 8$

---

7 .

3 more join in.

How many in all?

$7 + 3 = \underline{\hphantom{00}}$

Guided Practice

Read the problem. Trace the circles that match the numbers in the problem. Add the numbers. Trace the number that tells how many there are now. Read the addition sentence.

Read the problem. Draw a picture to match the problem. Write the number that tells how many there are in all. Read the addition sentence.

3 .

6 more join in.

How many in all? $3 + 6 = $ _____

---

5 .

2 more join in.

How many in all? $5 + 2 = $ _____

MP5

_____ .

_____ more join in.

How many in all? _____ + _____ = _____

Guided Practice

Read the problem. Draw a picture to match the problem. Add. Write the number that tells how many there are in all. Read the addition sentence.

Fill in numbers for the problem. Draw a picture to match the problem. Complete the addition sentence to match the problem.

Lesson 19 — Take Away to Subtract

Learn to take away.

K.OA.1

3 take away **1** **2** left

take away left

take away left

Guided Instruction Take away to find how many are left.

There are 3 children in all. How many children are leaving? Take them away. How many children are left? Trace the number that tells how many children are left.

Trace the number that tells how many children there are in all. Trace the number that tells how many children are taken away. Trace the number that tells how many children are left.

Unit 2 ■ Focus on Operations and Algebraic Thinking **91**

2 take away 1 equals _____ left

4 take away 2 equals _____ left

_____ take away _____ equals _____ left

Guided Instruction

 Trace the number that tells how many in all.
Trace the number that tells how many are leaving.
Write the number that tells how many are left.

Write the number that tells how many in all. Write the
number that tells how many are leaving. Write the
number that tells how many are left.

4 take away 3 1 left

___ ___ take away ___ ___ ___ ___ left

___ ___ take away ___ ___ ___ ___ left

Guided Practice

♥ Trace the number that tells how many frogs in all. Trace the number that tells how many frogs are leaving. Trace the number that tells how many frogs are left.

🦋 🧸 Write the number that tells how many in all. Write the number that tells how many are leaving. Write the number that tells how many are left.

_____   _____   _____

_ _ _ _ _   _ _ _ _ _   _ _ _ _ _

_____ take away   _____   _____ left

_____   _____   _____

_ _ _ _ _   _ _ _ _ _   _ _ _ _ _

_____ take away   _____   _____ left

Noah's Paper   Sofia's Paper
3 take away 1 2 left   4 take away 1 3 left

Guided Practice

♥ 🦋 Write the number that tells how many in all. Write the number that tells how many are leaving. Take away the ones that are leaving. Write the number that tells how many are left.

🧸 Noah and Sofia wrote numbers to match the picture of the ducks. Circle the paper that matches the picture. Explain what the other child did wrong.

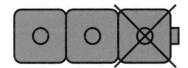

Lesson 20
Subtract to Find How Many Left

Learn to subtract.
K.OA.1

$$3 \;-\; 1 \;=\; 2$$

minus   equals

$$5 \;-\; 2 \;=\; 3$$

minus   equals

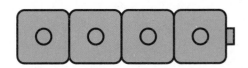

$$4 \;-\; 2 \;=\; \underline{\qquad}$$

minus   equals

Guided Instruction **Subtract to find how many are left. Introduce the minus sign.**

♥ How many cubes are there in all? The X is on the cubes being taken away. How many cubes are being taken away? Subtract 3 − 1 to find how many are left. Trace the number that tells how many cubes are left.

🦋 How many cubes are there in all? How many cubes are being taken away? Trace the X on each cube being

taken away. Trace the number that tells how many cubes are left.

🧸 How many cubes are there in all? How many cubes are being taken away? Draw an X on each cube being taken away. Write the number that tells how many cubes are left.

Unit 2 ■ Focus on Operations and Algebraic Thinking   **95**

$2 - 1 =$ ⊥

$5 - 3 =$ 2

$4 - 1 = $ ____

Guided Instruction

  How many cubes are there in all? Trace the X on the cubes being taken away. How many cubes are being taken away? Subtract 2 – 1 to find how many are left. Trace the number that tells how many cubes are left.

 How many cubes are there in all? How many cubes are being taken away? Draw an X on each cube being taken away. Write the number that tells how many cubes are left.

$$5 - 5 = 0$$

$$3 - 2 = \underline{}$$

$$4 - 4 = \underline{}$$

Guided Practice

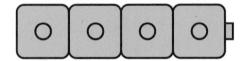 How many cubes are there in all? How many cubes are being taken away? Trace the X on each cube being taken away. How many cubes are being taken away? Subtract 5 – 5 to find how many are left. Trace the number that tells how many cubes are left.

How many cubes are there in all? How many cubes are being taken away? Draw an X on each cube being taken away. Write the number that tells how many cubes are left.

5 – 1 = _____

4 – 3 = _____

MP4

5 – 4 = _____

Guided Practice

How many cubes are there in all? How many cubes are being taken away? Draw an X on each cube being taken away. Write the number that tells how many cubes are left.

Look at the subtraction sentence. Draw a picture to show how many in all. Draw an X on each cube that is being taken away. Write how many are left.

Problem Solving: Subtraction

Learn to solve problems with subtraction.

K.OA.2

7 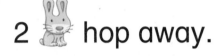.

2 🐰 hop away.

How many 🐰 left?

$7 - 2 = 5$ 🐰

5 🐝 .

3 🐝 fly away.

How many 🐝 left?

$5 - 3 = \underline{}$

Guided Instruction **Solve problems with subtraction.**

Introduce the term **subtraction sentence**.

♥ 🦋 Read the problem. Trace the circles that match the numbers in the problem.
Trace the X on each circle you want to take away. Subtract the numbers.
Trace or write the number that tells how many are left.
Read the subtraction sentence.

8 .

4  fly away.

How many  left?

$$8 - 4 = \underline{}$$

---

10 .

3  go away.

How many  now?

$$10 - 3 = \underline{}$$

Guided Instruction

  Read the problem. Trace the circles that match the numbers in the problem.
Trace the X on each circle you want to take away. Subtract the numbers.
Trace or write the number that tells how many are left.
Read the subtraction sentence.

7 .

4 🦋 fly away.

How many 🦋 left?

$$7 - 4 = 3$$ 🦋

🦋

4 🐟 .

1 🐟 swims away.

How many 🐟 now?

$$4 - 1 = \underline{\qquad}$$ 🐟

Guided Practice

🧡 Read the problem. Trace the circles that match the numbers in the problem. Trace the X on each circle you want to take away. Subtract the numbers. Trace the number that tells how many are left. Read the subtraction sentence.

🦋 Read the problem. Draw a picture to match the problem. Write the number that tells how many are left. Read the subtraction sentence.

9 .

6 run away.

How many left?   9 − 6 = _____

8 .

5 walk away.

How many left?   8 − 5 = _____

MP5

_____
_____ .

_____ run away.

How many are left? _____   _____ − _____ = _____

Guided Practice

  Read the problem. Draw a picture to match the problem. Write the number that tells how many left. Read the subtraction sentence.

 Fill in numbers for the problem. Draw a picture to match the problem. Complete the subtraction sentence to match the problem.

$3 =$  $+$

$3 =$ $+$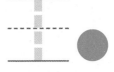

$3 =$ $+$

$3 =$ $+$

Guided Instruction   Break apart numbers.

♥ Look at the number 3. Color one circle yellow and the rest red. Trace the numbers that tell how many yellow circles and how many red circles.

🦋 Look at the number 3. Color two circles yellow and the rest red. Trace the numbers that tell how many yellow circles and how many red circles.

🧸 Look at the number 3. Color three circles yellow and the rest red. Write the numbers that tell how many yellow circles and how many red circles.

🦆 Look at the number 3. Color 0 circles yellow and the rest red. Trace the numbers that tell how many yellow circles and how many red circles.

Unit 2 ■ Focus on Operations and Algebraic Thinking   **103**

♥
1 = 0 ⬤ + ___ ⬤

🦋
1 = 1 ⬤ + ___ ⬤

🧸
2 = 0 ⬤ + 2 ⬤

🦆
2 = ___ ⬤ + ___ ⬤

⭐
2 = ___ ⬤ + ___ ⬤

Guided Instruction

♥ Color the circle red. Trace/write the numbers that tell how many yellow circles and how many red circles.

🦋 Color the circle yellow. Trace/write the numbers that tell how many yellow circles and how many red circles.

🧸 Color 2 circles red. Trace the numbers that tell how many yellow circles and how many red circles.

🦆 Color one circle yellow and the rest red. Write the numbers that tell how many yellow circles and how many red circles.

⭐ Color two circles yellow and the rest red. Write the numbers that tell how many yellow circles and how many red circles.

🔵🔵🔵🔵🔵 $5 = 0 + 5$

 ⭕⭕⭕⭕⭕ $5 = 1 + 4$

 ⭕⭕⭕⭕⭕ $5 = \underline{} + \underline{}$

 ⭕⭕⭕⭕⭕ $5 = \underline{} + \underline{}$

 ⭕⭕⭕⭕⭕ $5 = \underline{} + \underline{}$

 ⭕⭕⭕⭕⭕ $5 = \underline{} + \underline{}$

Guided Practice

♥ Color five circles red. Trace the numbers that tell how many yellow circles and how many red circles.

🦋 Color one circle yellow and 4 circles red. Trace the numbers that tell how many yellow circles and how many red circles.

 Color one more circle yellow than the last problem. Color the rest red. Write the numbers that tell how many yellow circles and how many red circles.

◯ ◯ ◯ ◯ $4 = \underline{\quad} + \underline{\quad}$

 ◯ ◯ ◯ ◯ $4 = \underline{\quad} + \underline{\quad}$

 ◯ ◯ ◯ ◯ $4 = \underline{\quad} + \underline{\quad}$

 ◯ ◯ ◯ ◯ $4 = \underline{\quad} + \underline{\quad}$

 ◯ ◯ ◯ ◯ $4 = \underline{\quad} + \underline{\quad}$

MP7

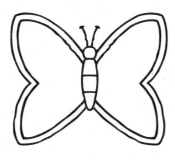   

Guided Practice

♥ Color four circles red. Write the numbers that tell how many yellow circles and how many red circles.

🦋🧸🦆⭐ Color one more circle yellow than the last problem. Color the rest red. Write the numbers that tell how many yellow circles and how many red circles.

🐢 Draw dots on the wings to show 2 different ways to have 3 dots on each butterfly.

Learn to add fluently.

K.OA.5

 ● ● ● ● ●

$2 + 3 = 5$

🦋 ● ● ●

$1 + 2 = 3$

 $4 + 0 = 4$

🦆 $3 + 1 = \underline{}$

★ $\begin{array}{r} 1 \\ + 3 \\ \hline 4 \end{array}$ ● ● ● ●

🐢 $\begin{array}{r} 3 \\ + 2 \\ \hline 5 \end{array}$ ● ● ● ● ●

 $\begin{array}{r} 0 \\ + 3 \\ \hline 3 \end{array}$

♣ $\begin{array}{r} 1 \\ + 4 \\ \hline \end{array}$

✿ $\begin{array}{r} 2 \\ + 2 \\ \hline \end{array}$

Guided Instruction **Fluently add sums to 5.**

Introduce the word **sum**.

♥ 🦋 🧸 Add. Trace the sum.
　　🦆 Add. Write the sum.
　　Introduce the vertical addition format.

★ 🐢 🐰 Add. Trace the sum.
♣ ✿ Add. Write the sum.

♥ $5 + 0 = 5$

🦋 $1 + 3 = 4$

🧸 $2 + 1 = \underline{\quad}$

🦆 $0 + 4 = \underline{\quad}$

⭐
$$\begin{array}{r} 0 \\ + 1 \\ \hline 1 \end{array}$$

🐢
$$\begin{array}{r} 4 \\ + 1 \\ \hline 5 \end{array}$$

🐰
$$\begin{array}{r} 0 \\ + 3 \\ \hline 3 \end{array}$$

♣
$$\begin{array}{r} 2 \\ + 2 \\ \hline \end{array}$$

✿
$$\begin{array}{r} 1 \\ + 0 \\ \hline \end{array}$$

🐦
$$\begin{array}{r} 2 \\ + 0 \\ \hline \end{array}$$

Guided Instruction

♥ 🦋 Add. Trace the sum.
🧸 🦆 Add. Write the sum.

⭐ 🐢 🐰 Add. Trace the sum.
♣ ✿ 🐦 Add. Write the sum.

Lesson 23 Addition: Sums to 5 (Fluency)

 1 + 1 = 2

1 + 4 = ___

 3 + 2 = ___

0 + 0 = ___

$$\begin{array}{r}3\\+0\\\hline\end{array}$$

$$\begin{array}{r}1\\+2\\\hline\end{array}$$

$$\begin{array}{r}0\\+2\\\hline\end{array}$$

$$\begin{array}{r}4\\+0\\\hline\end{array}$$

$$\begin{array}{r}2\\+3\\\hline\end{array}$$

$$\begin{array}{r}1\\+3\\\hline\end{array}$$

Guided Practice

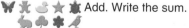 Add. Trace the sum.
Add. Write the sum.

♥ $4 + 1 = \underline{\quad}$

🦋 $2 + 2 = \underline{\quad}$

🧸 $0 + 2 = \underline{\quad}$

🦆 $3 + 2 = \underline{\quad}$

⭐

$$\begin{array}{r} 5 \\ +\,0 \\ \hline \\ \underline{\quad} \end{array}$$

🐢

$$\begin{array}{r} 1 \\ +\,3 \\ \hline \\ \underline{\quad} \end{array}$$

🐰

$$\begin{array}{r} 2 \\ +\,1 \\ \hline \\ \underline{\quad} \end{array}$$

☘
MP8

$0 + 3 = ?$ $2 + 0 = ?$

$0 + 5 = ?$ $0 + 1 = ?$

Guided Practice

♥ 🦋 🧸 🦆 Add. Write the sum.
⭐ 🐢 🐰

☘ Maria says she can add these facts very quickly. Explain how you think she can do it. Then see how fast you can say the sums aloud.

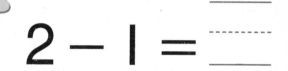

Learn to subtract fluently.

K.OA.5

 $4 - 2 = 2$

$3 - 0 = 3$

$5 - 3 = 2$

$2 - 1 = \underline{\hspace{1cm}}$

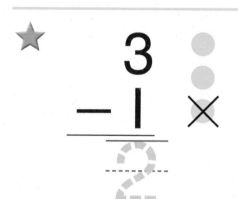

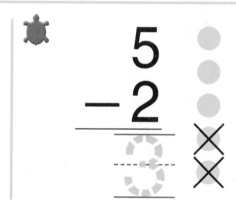

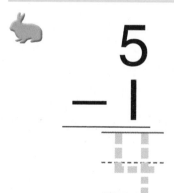

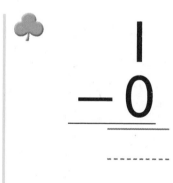

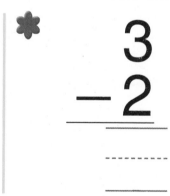

Guided Instruction **Fluently subtract from 5 or less.**

Introduce the word **difference**.

♥ 🦋 🧸 Subtract. Trace the difference.
　🦆 Subtract. Write the difference.
　　Introduce the vertical subtraction format.

⭐ 🐢 🐰 Subtract. Trace the difference.
♣ ❀ Subtract. Write the difference.

$5 - 5 = 0$ $1 - 0 = 1$

$4 - 1 = \underline{\quad}$ $5 - 3 = \underline{\quad}$

$$\begin{array}{r} 4 \\ -\ 4 \\ \hline 0 \end{array}$$ $$\begin{array}{r} 3 \\ -\ 2 \\ \hline 1 \end{array}$$ $$\begin{array}{r} 0 \\ -\ 0 \\ \hline 0 \end{array}$$

 $$\begin{array}{r} 5 \\ -\ 4 \\ \hline \end{array}$$ $$\begin{array}{r} 4 \\ -\ 0 \\ \hline \end{array}$$ $$\begin{array}{r} 5 \\ -\ 1 \\ \hline \end{array}$$

Guided Instruction

♥ 🦋 Subtract. Trace the difference.
🧸 🦆 Subtract. Write the difference.

⭐ 🐢 🐰 Subtract. Trace the difference.
♣ ✿ 🐦 Subtract. Write the difference.

♥ 5 − 1 =

 3 − 2 = _____

🧸 2 − 2 = _____

🦆 4 − 3 = _____

★
  5
− 5
_____

🐢
  3
− 0
_____

🐰
  2
− 1
_____

♣
  1
− 0
_____

✿
  5
− 3
_____

🐦
  4
− 2
_____

Guided Practice

♥ Subtract. Trace the difference.
Subtract. Write the difference.

♥
$$5 - 4 = \underline{}$$

🦋
$$3 - 1 = \underline{}$$

🧸
$$4 - 1 = \underline{}$$

🦆
$$4 - 4 = \underline{}$$

★
$$\begin{array}{r} 5 \\ -2 \\ \hline \end{array}$$

🐢
$$\begin{array}{r} 3 \\ -0 \\ \hline \end{array}$$

🐇
$$\begin{array}{r} 0 \\ -0 \\ \hline \end{array}$$

♣ MP8
$$5 - 5 = ?\quad 2 - 2 = ?\quad 3 - 3 = ?$$

$$\underline{} - \underline{} = \underline{}$$

Guided Practice

♥🦋🧸🦆★🐢🐇 Subtract. Write the difference.

♣ Chan says he can subtract these facts very quickly. Explain how you think he can do it. Then write another subtraction fact that he could answer very quickly.

Break Apart Numbers to 10

Learn to break apart numbers to 10.

K.OA.3

$$6 = 4 + 2$$

$$6 = 3 + 3$$

$$7 = 1 + \_\_$$

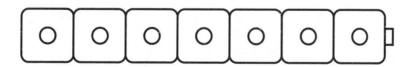

$$7 = \_\_ + \_\_$$

Guided Instruction **Break apart numbers to 10.**

   Trace the line to make 2 parts. Color each part a different color.
Trace/write the numbers that tell how many cubes are in each part.

 Draw a line to make 2 parts. Color each part a different color.
Write the numbers that tell how many cubes are in each part.

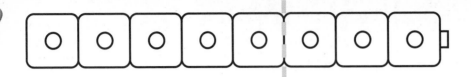

$$8 = 5 + \underline{\quad}$$

$$8 = 7 + \underline{\quad}$$

$$9 = \underline{\quad} + \underline{\quad}$$

$$9 = \underline{\quad} + \underline{\quad}$$

Guided Instruction

♥ ✖ Trace the line to make 2 parts. Color each part a different color.
Trace or write the numbers that tell how many cubes are in each part.

🧸 Trace the line to make 2 parts. Color each part a different color.
Write the numbers that tell how many cubes are in each part.

🦆 Draw a line to make 2 parts. Color each part a different color.
Write the numbers that tell how many cubes are in each part.

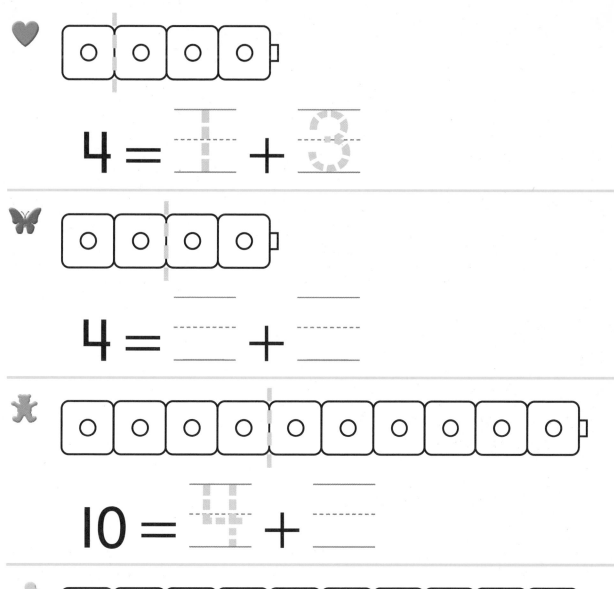

♥ $4 = 1 + 3$

🦋 $4 = \underline{} + \underline{}$

🧸 $10 = 5 + \underline{}$

🦆 $10 = \underline{} + \underline{}$

Guided Practice

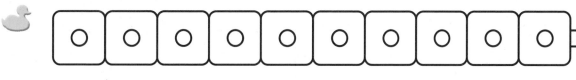

♥ Trace the line to make 2 parts. Color each part a different color. Trace the numbers that tell how many cubes are in each part.

🦋 Trace the line to make 2 parts. Color each part a different color. Write the numbers that tell how many cubes are in each part.

🧸 Trace the line to make 2 parts. Color each part a different color. Trace or write the numbers that tell how many cubes are in each part.

🦆 Draw a line to make 2 parts. Color each part a different color. Write the numbers that tell how many cubes are in each part.

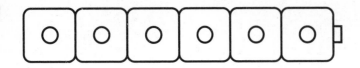

♥
6 = ___ + ___

6 = ___ + ___

3 = ___ + ___

 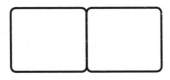 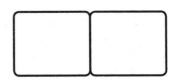
MP7

7 = ___ + ___   7 = ___ + ___

Guided Practice

♥ 🦋 🧸 Draw a line to make 2 parts. Color each part a different color.
Write the numbers that tell how many cubes are in each part.

🦆 Show the number 7 two ways. Draw dots on each side of the dominoes.
Write the numbers that tell how many dots are on each side.

Learn to make 10.

K.OA.4

$$3 + 7 = 10$$

$$6 + 4 = 10$$

$$1 + \underline{\quad} = 10$$

Guided Instruction   **Make 10 from a given number.**

Read the number that tells how many beads are purple. Color the rest of the beads yellow. Trace the number that tells how many are yellow. Tell how many beads there are in all.

Read the number that tells how many beads are green. Color the rest of the beads orange. Write the number that tells how many beads are orange. Tell how many beads there are in all.

$$9 + \underline{1} = 10$$

$$4 + \underline{} = 10$$

$$8 + \underline{} = 10$$

Guided Instruction

♥ 🧸 🦋 Read the number that tells how many beads there are. Trace/draw more beads to make 10 in all. Trace/write the number that tells how many beads you drew.

$$2 + 8 = 10$$

$$5 + \underline{} = 10$$

$$7 + \underline{} = 10$$

Guided Practice

♥ Read the number that tells how many train cars are orange. Color the rest of the train cars blue. Trace the number that tells how many train cars are blue. Tell how many train cars there are in all.

🦋 🧸 Read the number that tells how many train cars are red. Color the rest of the train cars a different color. Write the number that tells how many train cars you colored. Tell how many train cars there are in all.

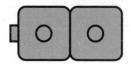

$$2 + \underline{\quad} = 10$$

$$6 + \underline{\quad} = 10$$

MP3

Guided Practice

♥ ✦ Read the number that tells how cubes there are. Draw more cubes to make 10 in all. Write the number that tells how many cubes you drew.

🐻 Zachery drew these apples. Ana says she will draw 6 more apples so there will be 10 in all. Draw to see if she is correct. Talk about your drawing.

_____   _____   _____
- - - - -   - - - - -   - - - - -
_____ and _____   _____ in all

_____   _____   _____
- - - - -   - - - - -   - - - - -
_____ take away _____   _____ left

2 .

7 more join them.

How many in all? _____

$2 + 7 =$ _____

💜 Write the numbers that tell how many marbles are in each group. Write the number that tells how many marbles in all.

🦋 Write the number that tells how many fish in all. Write the number that tells how many fish are leaving. Write the number that tells how many fish are left.

🧸 Read the problem. Draw a picture to match the problem. Write the number that tells how many there are in all. Read the addition sentence.

Unit 2 ■ Focus on Operations and Algebraic Thinking **123**

8 🐱.

3 🐱 run away.

How many 🐱 are left? _____

$8 - 3 = $ _____ 🐱

$5 = $ _____ $+$ _____

$9 = $ _____ $+$ _____

💜 Read the problem. Draw a picture to match the problem. Write the number that tells how many left. Read the subtraction sentence.

🦋 🧸 Draw a line to make 2 parts. Color each part a different color. Write the numbers that tell how many cubes are in each part.

♥ $3 + 1 = $ ___   🦋 $3 + 0 = $ ___

🧸 $5 - 2 = $ ___   🦆 $3 - 2 = $ ___

⭐
$$\begin{array}{r} 0 \\ +\ 5 \\ \hline \end{array}$$

🐢
$$\begin{array}{r} 3 \\ +\ 2 \\ \hline \end{array}$$

🐰
$$\begin{array}{r} 2 \\ +\ 2 \\ \hline \end{array}$$

♣
$$\begin{array}{r} 2 \\ -\ 0 \\ \hline \end{array}$$

✿
$$\begin{array}{r} 2 \\ -\ 2 \\ \hline \end{array}$$

🐦
$$\begin{array}{r} 5 \\ -\ 3 \\ \hline \end{array}$$

♥ 🦋 Add. Write the sum.
🧸 🦆 Subtract. Write the difference.

⭐ 🐢 🐰 Add. Write the sum.
♣ ✿ 🐦 Subtract. Write the difference.

MP7

MP5

_____

_____ .
_____

_____ more 🐰 come.

How many 🐰 in all?

_____   _____   _____

___ **+** ___ **=** ___

MP4

4 − 3 = _____

MP3

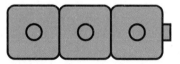

 Draw dots on the domino parts to show two different ways to have 4 dots on each domino.

 Fill in numbers for the problem. Draw a picture to match the problem. Complete the addition sentence to match the problem.

Look at the subtraction sentence. Draw a picture to show how many in all. Draw an X to show how many are being taken away. Write how many are left.

Jake made this cube train. Liam says he will draw 7 more cubes so there will be 10 in all. Draw to see if Liam is correct. Tell about your drawing.

Progress Check

In this unit you will learn about Number and Operations in Base Ten. The lessons in this unit cover all the Common Core Standards for Number and Operations in Base Ten.

To practice your skills, go to sadlierconnect.com.

Before Unit 3	Can I ?	After Unit 3
☐	**Count and model** 11, 12, 13, 14, 15, 16, 17, 18, 19, 20 K.NBT.1, K.CC.4, K.CC.5	☐
☐	**Count and write** 11, 12, 13, 14, 15, 16, 17, 18, 19, 20 K.CC.3, K.CC.5	☐
☐	Count to 100 K.CC.1, K.CC.2	☐
☐	Show numbers 11 through 19 as ten ones and some more ones K.NBT.1	☐

In this unit your child will:

- Count to 100 by ones and by tens.

- Count forward from any starting number.

- Count to tell the number of objects in a group of up to 20 objects.

- Show up to 20 objects.

- Read and write numbers to 20.

- Make or break apart numbers into 10 ones and some more ones.

Note: All of these learning goals for your child are based on the Grade K Common Core State Standards for Mathematics.

Your child is introduced to the basic concept of place value. While counting, modeling, reading, and writing numbers as before, an understanding is also built that each number between 11 and 19 is composed of 10 ones and some more ones. So, your child might model and record the number 13 as shown:

$$13 = 10 + 3$$

This thinking will help as your child learns to count by both ones and tens.

Ways to Help Your Child

Your child might benefit from practicing the counting sequence. You can suggest engaging ways to count aloud that includes movements he or she enjoys such as clapping, jumping, or marching in place. A fun way to count by tens to 100 is to whisper "one, two, three," and so on through 9, and then jump and shout "ten."

Activity: Suggest a number hunt to locate between 11 and 19 of any object. After counting to confirm the number, your child can make a picture by drawing, writing, or gluing to show the number of objects. Suggest that your child identify "ten ones" in the number by drawing a ring around 10 of the objects in his or her picture.

ONLINE

For more Home Connect activities, continue online at sadlierconnect.com

Focus on Number and Operations in Base Ten

Essential Question:
How can you use a 10 to show a number?

Number and Operations in Base Ten

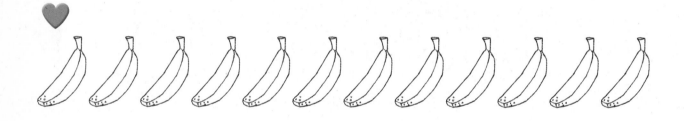

Count the apples. There are 10 apples.

♥ 🦋 Color a group of 10.

Learn about 11 and 12.

K.NBT.1, K.CC.4, K.CC.5

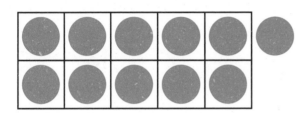

$$10 + 1 = 11$$

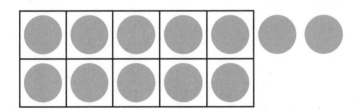

$$10 + 2 = 12$$

Guided Instruction **Count to find how many in all.**

Count the counters in the ten frame. Then count how many more ones. Trace the number that tells how many counters are in the ten frame. Trace the number that tells how many more ones. Read the addition sentence: Ten plus one equals eleven. Look at the number 11 and the number name **eleven**.

Count the counters in the ten frame. Then count how many more ones. Trace the number that tells how many counters are in the ten frame. Trace the number that tells how many more ones. Read the addition sentence: Ten plus two equals twelve. Look at the number 12 and the number name **twelve**.

$$12 = 10 + \underline{\quad}$$

$$11 = 10 + \underline{\quad}$$

$$10 + \underline{\quad} = 12$$

Guided Instruction

 Count the flowers. Draw more to make 12. Write the number that tells how many more you drew to make 12.

 Count the flowers. Draw more to make 11. Write the number that tells how many more you drew to make 11.

 Circle 10 socks. Write the number that tells how many more to make 12 socks.

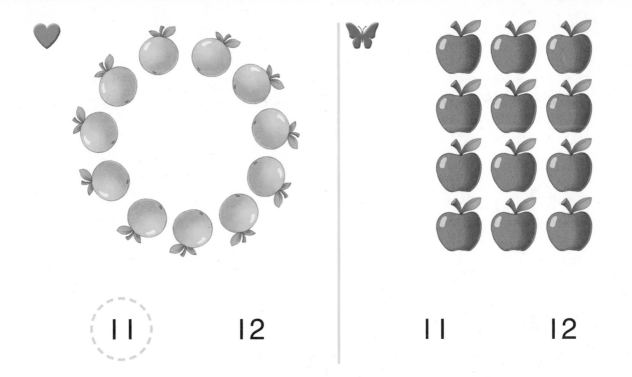

♥   11   12   🦋   11   12

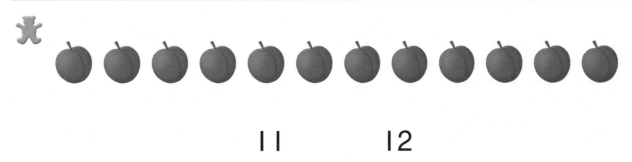

🧸   11   12

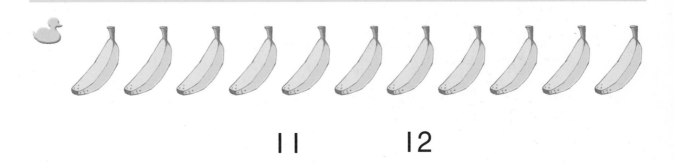

🦆   11   12

Guided Practice

♥ 🦋 🧸 🦆 Count the fruit. Circle the number that tells how many.

$$10 + \underline{\quad} = 11$$

$$10 + \underline{\quad} = 12$$

MP1

$$\underline{\quad}$$ eggs left

Guided Practice

♥ 🦋 Circle 10 bugs. Write the number that tells how many more to make 11 (12) bugs in all.

🧸 Zoe's mother bought a carton with 12 eggs. She uses 10 eggs. Circle the eggs she uses. Write the number that tells how many eggs she has left.

Learn to write 11 and 12.

K.CC.3, K.CC.5

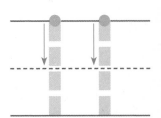

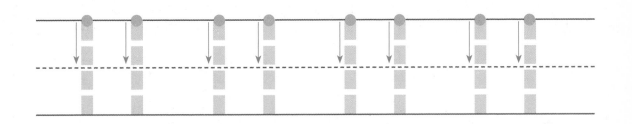

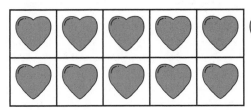

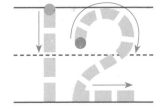

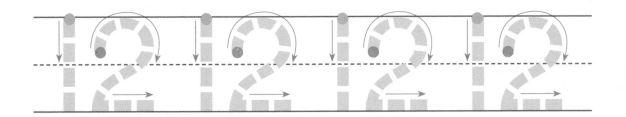

Guided Instruction **Write numbers to tell how many.**

♥ Count how many stars. There are 11 stars. Trace the number 11.
Trace the other 11s.

🦋 Count how many hearts. There are 12 hearts. Trace the number 12.
Trace the other 12s.

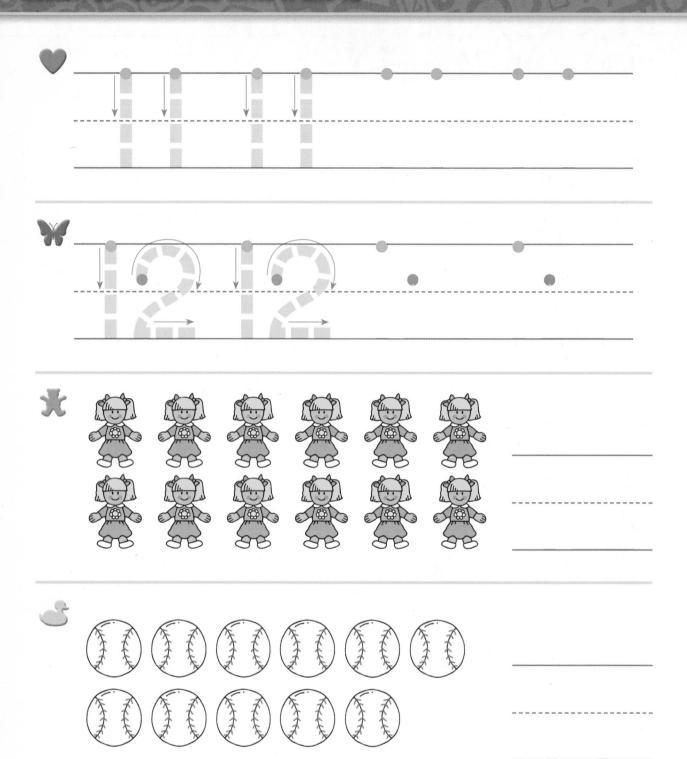

Guided Instruction

♥ Trace the 11s. Start at each blue dot to write more 11s.
🦋 Trace the 12s. Start at each blue dot to write more 12s.
🧸 Count how many dolls. Write the number that tells how many.
🦆 Count how many baseballs. Write the number that tells how many.

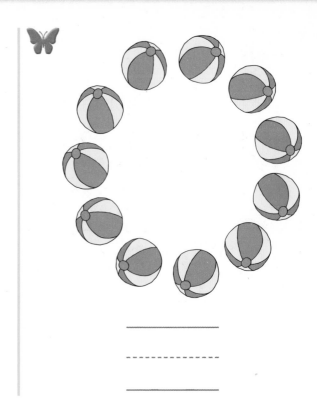

12

Guided Practice

♥ 🦋 🧸 🦆 Count how many. Trace/write the number that tells how many.

_____

- - - - - - - - - - - - - -

_____

_____

- - - - - - - - - - - - - -

_____

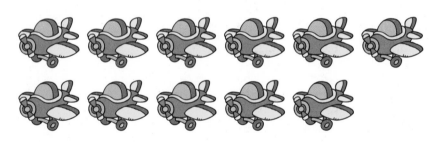

_____

- - - - - - - - - - - - - -

_____

MP1

_____   _____

- - - - - - - - - - -   - - - - - - - - - - -

_____   _____

Guided Practice

♥ 🦋 🧸 Count how many. Write the number that tells how many.
🦆 Write the numbers 11 and 12. Circle the number that has only straight lines.

Count and Model 13 and 14

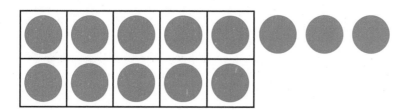

13
thirteen

$$10 + 3 = 13$$

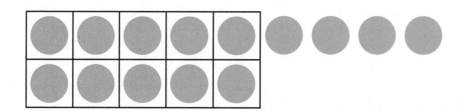

14
fourteen

$$10 + 4 = 14$$

Guided Instruction **Count to find how many in all.**

Count the counters in the ten frame. Then count how many more ones. Trace the number that tells how many counters are in the ten frame. Trace the number that tells how many more ones. Read the addition sentence: Ten plus three equals thirteen. Look at the number **13** and the number name **thirteen**.

Count the counters in the ten frame. Then count how many more ones. Trace the number that tells how many counters are in the ten frame. Trace the number that tells how many more ones. Read the addition sentence: Ten plus four equals fourteen. Look at the number **14** and the number name **fourteen**.

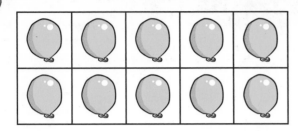

$$13 = 10 + \underline{\quad}$$

$$14 = 10 + \underline{\quad}$$

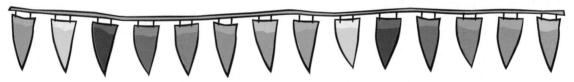

$$10 + \underline{\quad} = 14$$

Guided Instruction

♥ Count the balloons. Draw more to make 13. Write the number that tells how many more you drew to make 13.

🦋 Count the balloons. Draw more to make 14. Write the number that tells how many more you drew to make 14.

🧸 Circle 10 flags. Write the number that tells how many more to make 14 flags in all.

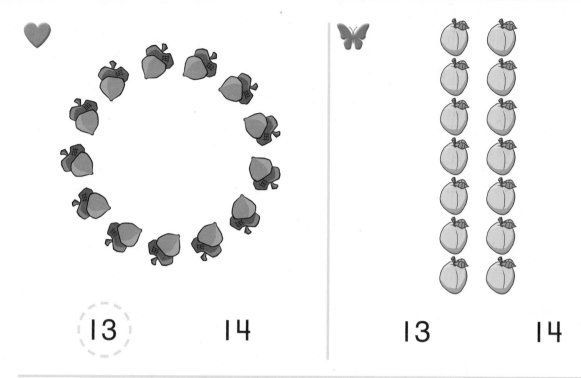

13   14   13   14

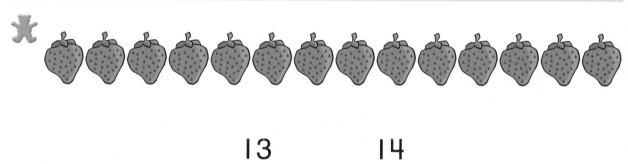

13   14

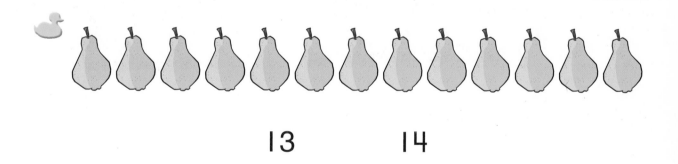

13   14

Guided Practice

♥ Count the acorns. Trace the circle around the number that tells how many.

🦋 🐻 🦆 Count the fruit. Circle the number that tells how many.

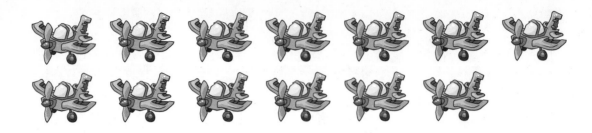

$$10 + \underline{\quad} = 13$$

$$10 + \underline{\quad} = 14$$

MP2

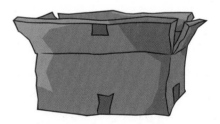

_____

_____ books left

Guided Practice

♥ ✿ Circle 10 toys. Write the number that tells how many more to make 13 (14) in all.

🧸 Ryan has 13 books on a shelf. He is going to put 10 of them in the box. Write the number that tells how many books will be left on the shelf.

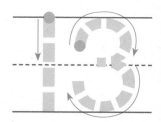

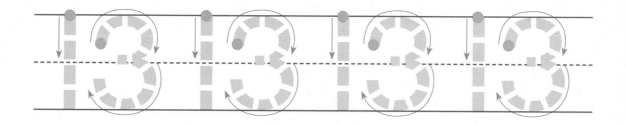

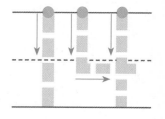

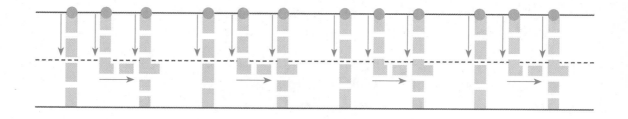

Guided Instruction **Write numbers to tell how many.**

 Count how many ladybugs. There are 13 ladybugs. Trace the number 13.
Trace the other 13s.

 Count how many bees. There are 14 bees. Trace the number 14.
Trace the other 14s.

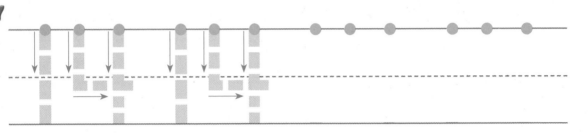

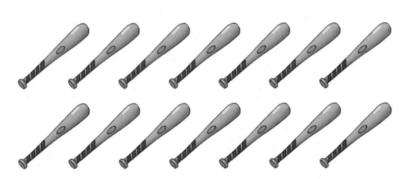

Guided Instruction

 Trace the 13s. Start at each blue dot to write more 13s.

Trace the 14s. Start at each blue dot to write more 14s.

Count how many baseball bats. Write the number that tells how many.

Count how many soccer balls. Write the number that tells how many.

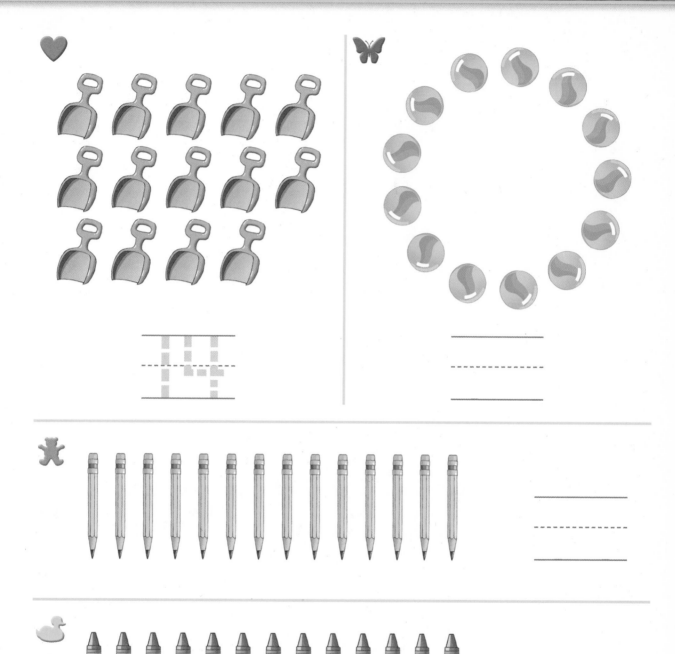

Guided Practice

♥ 🦋 🧸 🦆 Count how many. Trace/write the number that tells how many.

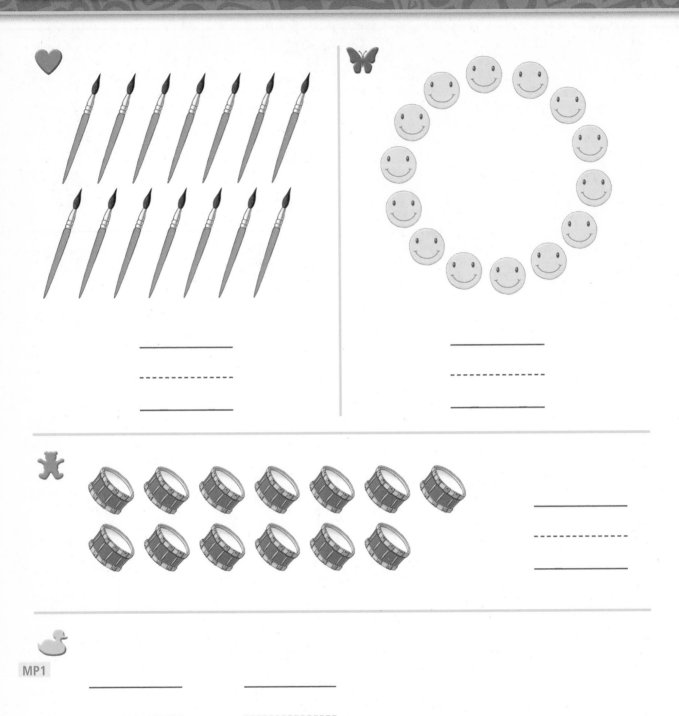

Guided Practice

♥ 🦋 🎷 Count how many. Write the number that tells how many.

🦆 Tami writes the numbers 13 and 14. She circles the number that has only straight lines. Write to show what is on Tami's paper.

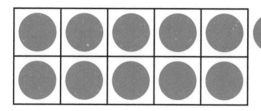

$$10 + 5 = 15$$

$$\text{15} \quad \text{fifteen}$$

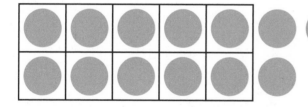

$$10 + 6 = 16$$

$$\text{16} \quad \text{sixteen}$$

Guided Instruction **Count to find how many in all.**

♥ Count the counters in the ten frame. Then count how many more ones. Trace the number that tells how many counters are in the ten frame. Trace the number that tells how many more ones. Read the addition sentence: Ten plus five equals fifteen. Look at the number **15** and the number name **fifteen**.

🦋 Count the counters in the ten frame. Then count how many more ones. Trace the number that tells how many counters are in the ten frame. Trace the number that tells how many more ones. Read the addition sentence: Ten plus six equals sixteen. Look at the number **16** and the number name **sixteen**.

Unit 3 ■ Focus on Number and Operations in Base Ten **147**

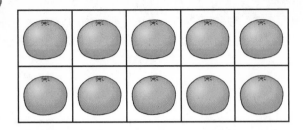

$$15 = 10 + \underline{}$$

$$16 = 10 + \underline{}$$

$$10 + \underline{} = 15$$

Guided Instruction

♥ Count the oranges. Draw more to make 15. Write the number that tells how many more you drew to make 15.

🦋 Count the apples. Draw more to make 16. Write the number that tells how many more you drew to make 16.

🧸 Circle 10 butterflies. Write the number that tells how many more to make 15 butterflies in all.

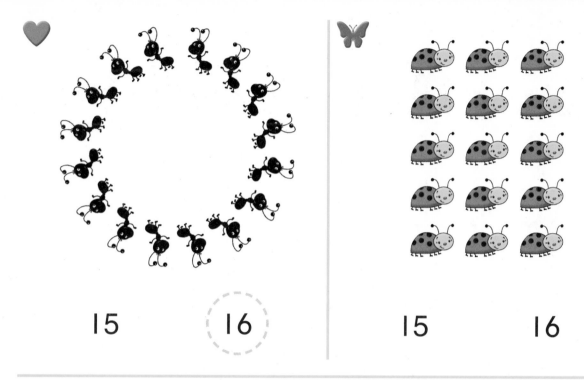

♥   15   ⟨16⟩   🦋   15   16

🧸   15   16

🦆   15   16

Guided Practice

♥ 🦋 🧸 🦆 Count the bugs. Circle the number that tells how many.

$$10 + \underline{\quad} = 15$$

$$10 + \underline{\quad} = 16$$

MP1

$$\underline{\qquad}$$ more

Guided Practice

♥ 🦋 Circle 10 animals. Write the number that tells how many more to make 15 (16) animals in all.

🧸 Hayley drew these happy faces. Write the number that tells how many more she needs to draw to make 16. Draw happy faces so that there are 16 in all.

Count and Write 15 and 16

Learn to write 15 and 16.

K.CC.3, K.CC.5

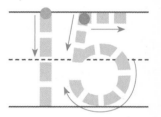

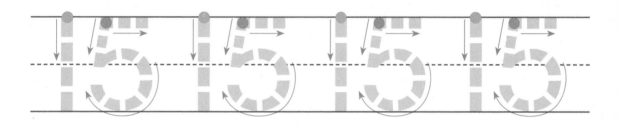

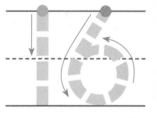

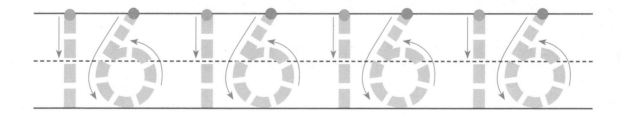

Guided Instruction **Write numbers to tell how many.**

♥ Count how many green marbles. There are 15 green marbles.
Trace the number 15. Trace the other 15s.

🦋 Count how many red marbles. There are 16 red marbles.
Trace the number 16. Trace the other 16s.

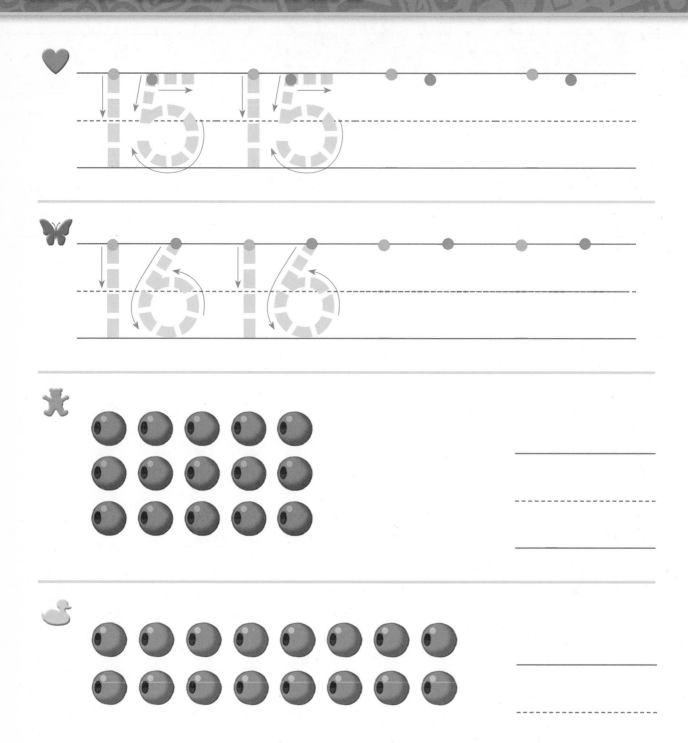

Guided Instruction

♥ Trace the 15s. Start at each blue dot to write more 15s.
🦋 Trace the 16s. Start at each blue dot to write more 16s.
🧸🦆 Count the beads. Write the number that tells how many.

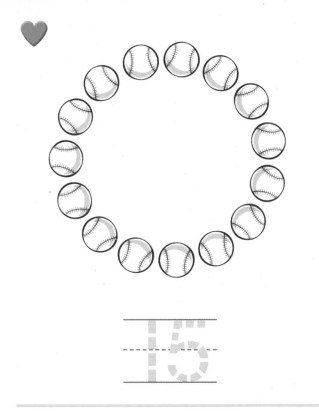

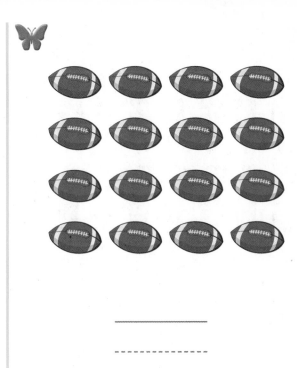

15

_____

_____

_____

Guided Practice

♥ 🦋 🧸 🦆 Count how many. Trace/write the number that tells how many.

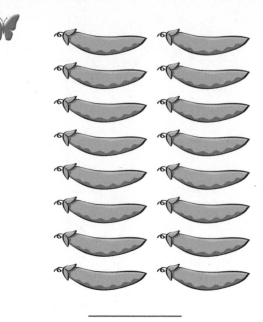

♥
_____

🦋
_____

🧸 _____

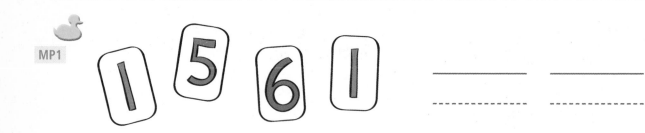

🦆

MP1

_____ _____

Guided Practice

♥ 🦋 🧸 Count how many. Write the number that tells how many.

🦆 Dennis puts 2 number cards together to make one number. Then he puts the other 2 number cards together to make another number. Write to show what numbers Dennis might have made.

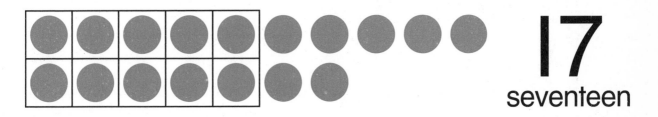

17 seventeen

$$10 + 7 = 17$$

18 eighteen

$$10 + 8 = 18$$

Guided Instruction **Count to find how many in all.**

♥ Count the counters in the ten frame. Then count how many more ones. Trace the number that tells how many counters are in the ten frame. Trace the number that tells how many more ones. Read the addition sentence: Ten plus seven equals seventeen. Look at the number **17** and the number name **seventeen**.

🦋 Count the counters in the ten frame. Then count how many more ones. Trace the number that tells how many counters are in the ten frame. Trace the number that tells how many more ones. Read the addition sentence: Ten plus eight equals eighteen. Look at the number **18** and the number name **eighteen**.

Unit 3 ■ Focus on Number and Operations in Base Ten **155**

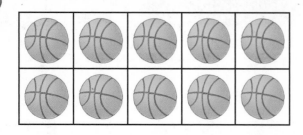

$$17 = 10 + \underline{}$$

$$18 = 10 + \underline{}$$

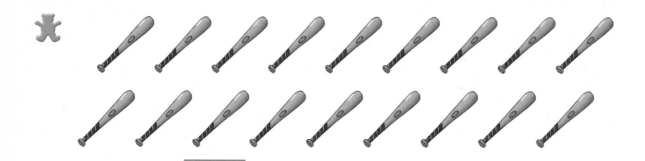

$$10 + \underline{} = 18$$

Guided Instruction

♥ Count the basketballs. Draw more to make 17. Write the number that tells how many more you drew to make 17.

🦋 Count the baseballs. Draw more to make 18. Write the number that tells how many more you drew to make 18.

🧸 Circle 10 baseball bats. Write the number that tells how many more to make 18 baseball bats in all.

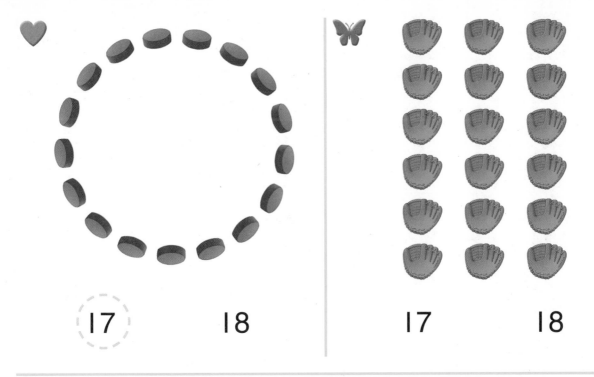

17   18   17   18

17   18

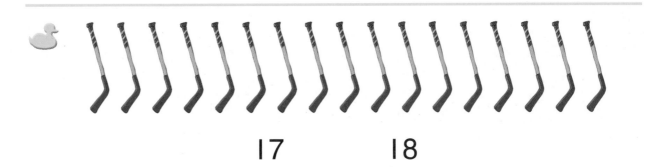

17   18

Guided Practice

❤ 🦋 🧸 🦆 Count the objects. Circle the number that tells how many.

$$10 + \underline{\quad} = 18$$

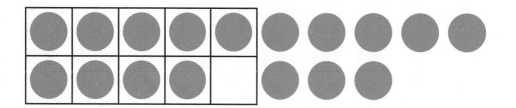

$$10 + \underline{\quad} = 17$$

MP2

Guided Practice

 Circle 10 shells. Write the number that tells how many more to make 18 shells in all.

Circle 10 fish. Write the number that tells how many more to make 17 fish in all.

Kevin has a ten frame with 9 counters. He gets 8 more counters. He says he has 18 counters. Is he right? Explain why or why not.

Count and Write
17 and 18

**Learn to write
17 and 18.**

K.CC.3, K.CC.5

♥

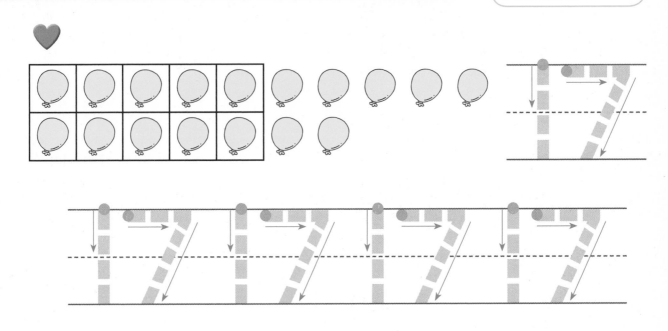

🦋

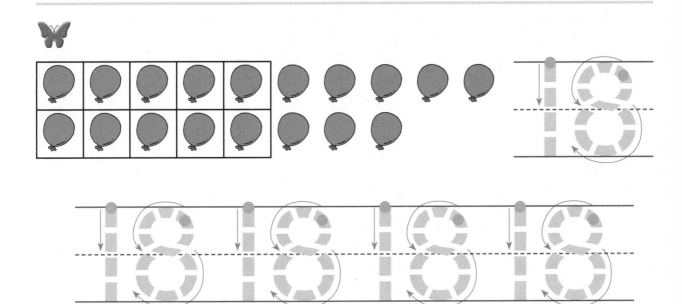

Guided Instruction **Write numbers to tell how many.**

♥ Count how many yellow balloons. There are 17 yellow balloons.
Trace the number 17. Trace the other 17s.

🦋 Count how many red balloons. There are 18 red balloons.
Trace the number 18. Trace the other 18s.

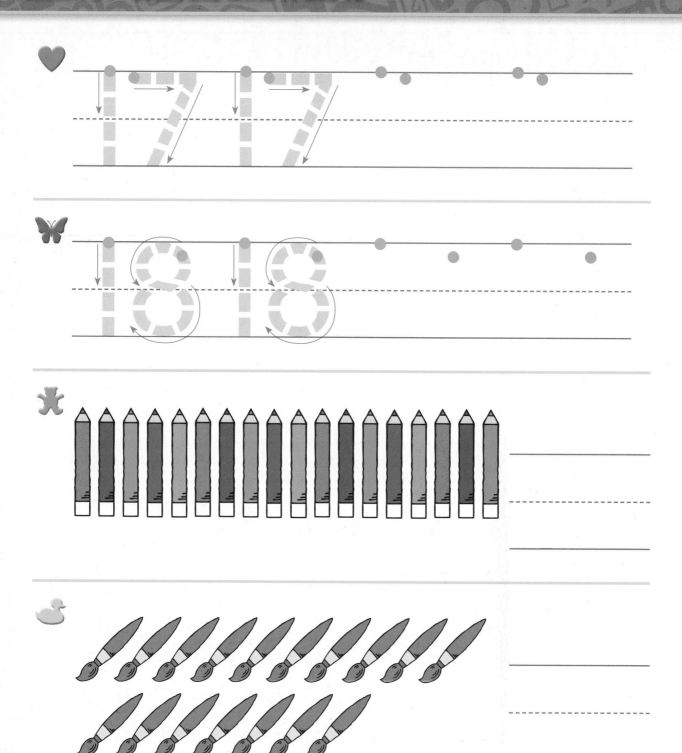

Guided Instruction

♥ Trace the 17s. Start at each blue dot to write more 17s.
🦋 Trace the 18s. Start at each blue dot to write more 18s.
🐻 Count the pencils. Write the number that tells how many.
🦆 Count the paintbrushes. Write the number that tells how many.

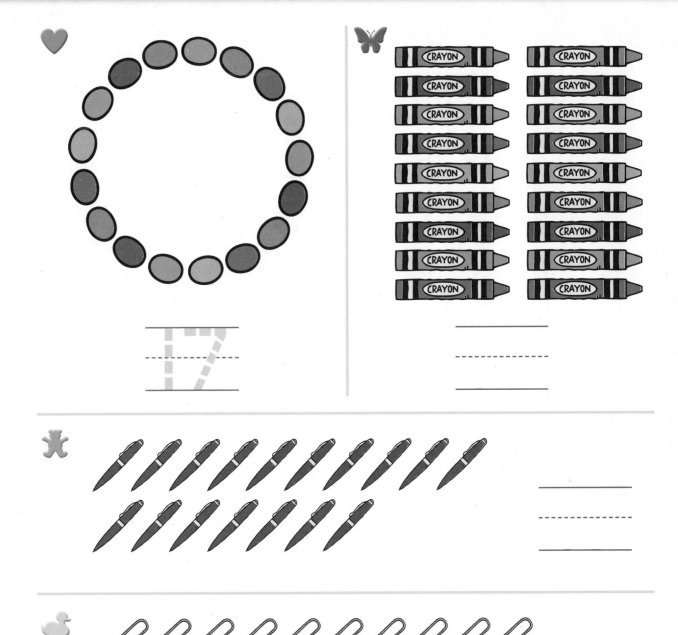

Guided Practice

♥ 🦋 🧸 🦆 Count how many. Trace/write the number that tells how many.

♥

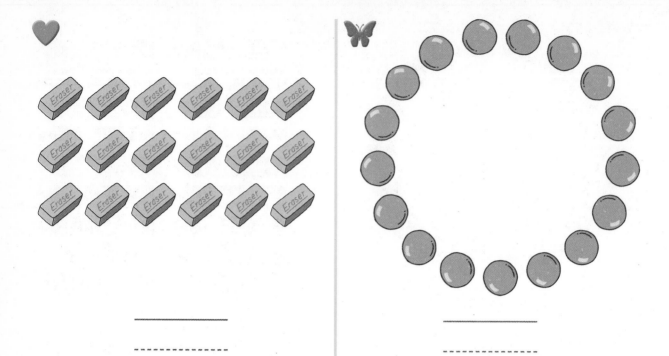

🦋

_____

- - - - - - - - - - -

_____

_____

- - - - - - - - - - -

_____

🧸

_____

- - - - - - - - - - -

_____

MP4

_____

- - - - - - - - - - -

_____

Guided Practice

♥ 🦋 🧸 Count how many. Write the number that tells how many.

🦆 Claudia draws a row of 9 dots. Then she draws another row of 9 dots. Draw what she drew. Then count and write how many.

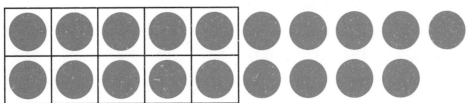

Learn about 19 and 20.

K.NBT.1, K.CC.4, K.CC.5

♥

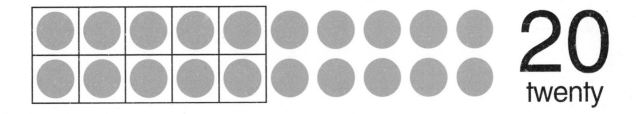

$$10 + 9 = 19$$

🦋

20
twenty

$$10 + 10 = 20$$

Guided Instruction Count to find how many in all.

♥ Count the counters in the ten frame. Then count how many more ones. Trace the number that tells how many counters are in the ten frame. Trace the number that tells how many more ones to make 19 in all. Read the addition sentence: Ten plus nine equals nineteen. Look at the number **19** and the number name **nineteen**.

🦋 Count the counters in the ten frame. Then count how many more ones. Trace the number that tells how many counters are in the ten frame. Trace the number that tells how many more ones to make 20 in all. Read the addition sentence: Ten plus ten equals twenty. Look at the number **20** and the number name **twenty**.

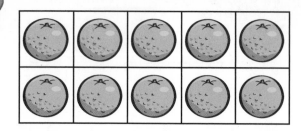

$$19 = 10 + \underline{}$$

 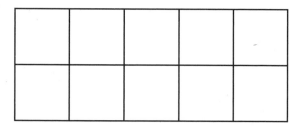

$$20 = 10 + \underline{}$$

$$10 + \underline{} = 19$$

Guided Instruction

 Count the oranges. Draw more to make 19. Write the number that tells how many more you drew to make 19.

 Count the apples. Draw more to make 20. Write the number that tells how many more you drew to make 20.

 Circle 10 bananas. Write the number that tells how many more there are.

164   Unit 3 ▪ Focus on Number and Operations in Base Ten

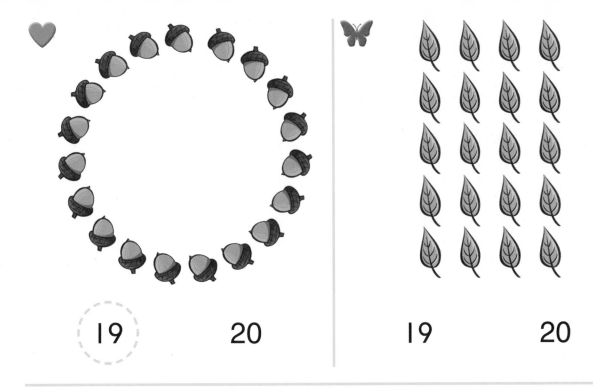

19   20

19   20

19   20

19   20

Guided Practice

♥ 🦋 🧸 🦆 Count the objects. Circle the number that tells how many.

$$10 + \underline{\quad} = 19$$

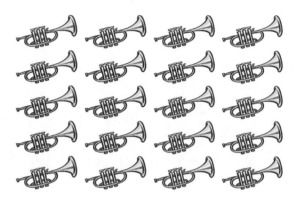

$$10 + \underline{\quad} = 20$$

MP2

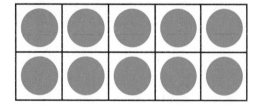 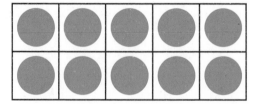

Guided Practice

♥ Circle 10 drums. Write the number that tells how many more to make 19 drums in all.

🦋 Circle 10 trumpets. Write the number that tells how many more to make 20 trumpets in all.

🧸 Mia has 2 full ten frames. She says she knows how many she has without counting. Explain how she can do that.

Learn to write 19 and 20.

K.CC.3, K.CC.5

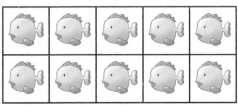  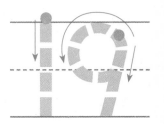

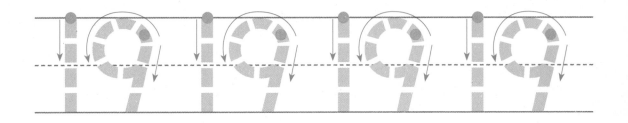

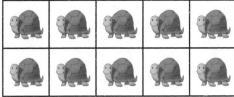  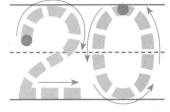

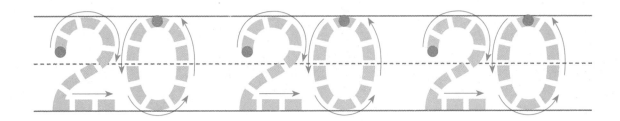

Guided Instruction **Write numbers to tell how many.**

 Count how many fish. There are 19 fish. Trace the number 19.
Trace the other 19s.

 Count how many turtles. There are 20 turtles. Trace the number 20.
Trace the other 20s.

Unit 3 ■ Focus on Number and Operations in Base Ten **167**

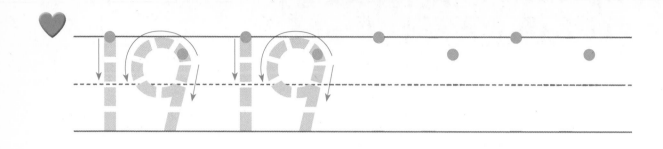

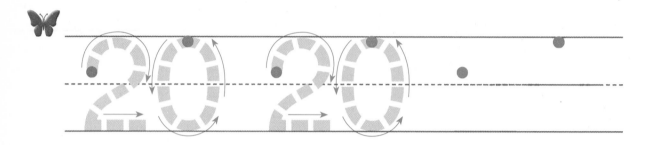

Guided Instruction

♥ Trace the 19s. Start at each blue dot to write more 19s.
🦋 Trace the 20s. Start at each blue dot to write more 20s.
🧸 Count the pails. Write the number that tells how many.
🦆 Count the shovels. Write the number that tells how many.

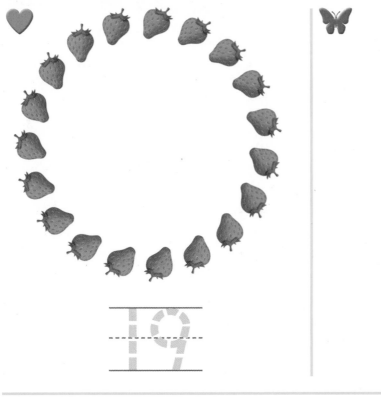

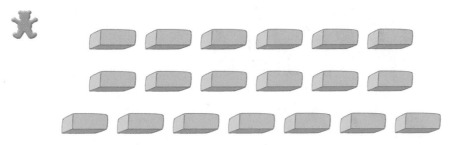

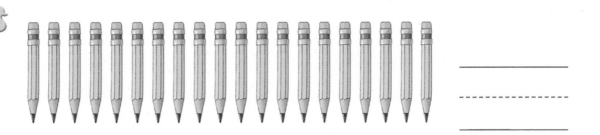

Guided Practice

♥ 🦋 🧸 🦆 Count how many. Write the number that tells how many.

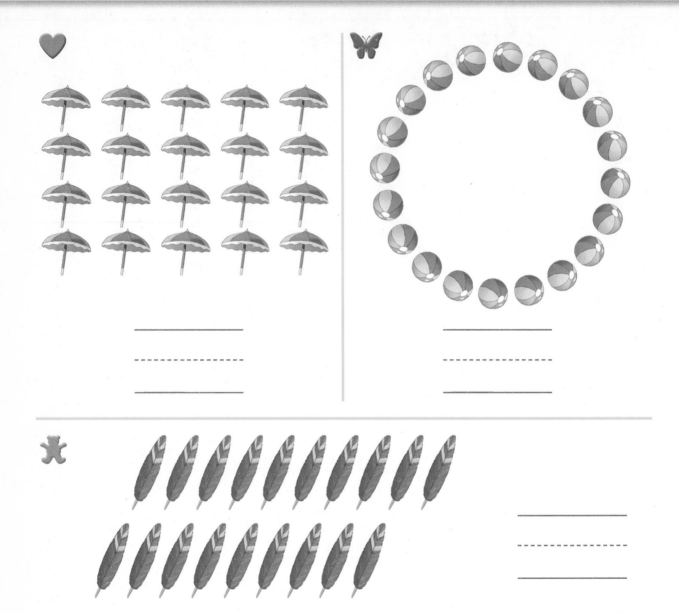

Guided Practice

♥ 🦋 🧸 Count how many. Write the number that tells how many.

🦆 Emma drew this row of flowers. Dylan drew the same number of flowers.
Draw the flowers that Dylan drew. Then count and write how many flowers in all.

Make and Break Apart 11 to 19

Learn to make and break apart 11-19.

K.NBT.1

 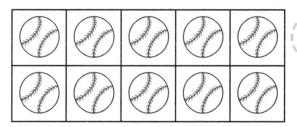

$$12 = 10 + \underline{2}$$

 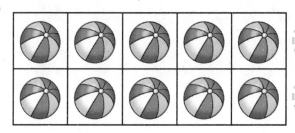

$$16 = 10 + \underline{}$$

 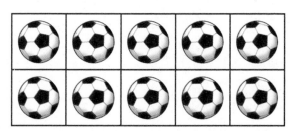

$$14 = 10 + \underline{}$$

Guided Instruction **Make and break apart numbers 11 to 19.**

♥ Count the baseballs. Trace more to make 12. Trace the number that tells how many more you drew to make 12.

🦋 Count the beach balls. Trace more to make 16. Write the number that tells how many more you drew to make 16.

🧸 Count the soccer balls. Draw more to make 14. Write the number that tells how many more you drew to make 14.

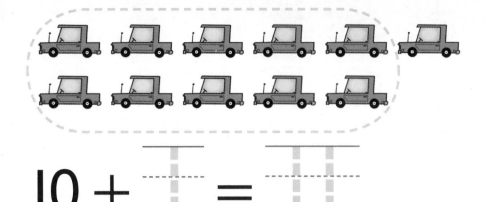

$$10 + \underline{\hspace{2cm}} = \underline{\hspace{2cm}}$$

$$10 + \underline{\hspace{2cm}} = \underline{\hspace{2cm}}$$

$$10 + \underline{\hspace{2cm}} = \underline{\hspace{2cm}}$$

Guided Instruction

Circle 10 cars. Write the number that tells how many more there are. Write the number that tells how many cars there are in all.

Circle 10 trucks. Write the number that tells how many more there are. Write the number that tells how many trucks there are in all.

Circle 10 buses. Write the number that tells how many more there are. Write the number that tells how many buses there are in all.

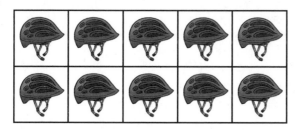

$$17 = 10 + 7$$

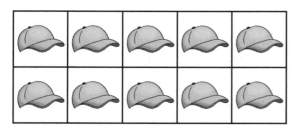

$$19 = 10 + \underline{}$$

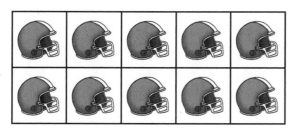

$$16 = 10 + \underline{}$$

Guided Practice

 Count the bicycle helmets. Draw more to make 17. Trace the number that tells how many more you drew to make 17.

 Count the football helmets. Draw more to make 19. Write the number that tells how many more you drew to make 19.

 Count the baseball hats. Draw more to make 16. Write the number that tells how many more you drew to make 16.

$$10 + \rule{1cm}{0.4pt} = \rule{1cm}{0.4pt}$$

$$10 + \rule{1cm}{0.4pt} = \rule{1cm}{0.4pt}$$

MP1

_____ counters

Guided Practice

♥ Circle 10 butterflies. Write the number that tells how many more there are. Write the number that tells how many there are in all.

🦋 Count the ladybugs. Draw more to make 11. Write the number that tells how many more you drew to make 11. Write the number that tells how many there are in all.

🧸 Lily has 8 counters. Tyler brings over a full 10 frame of counters. How many counters do they have together?

1	2	3	4	5	6	7	8	9	10
11	12	13	14	15	16	17	18	19	20
21	22	23	24	25	26	27	28	29	30
31	32	33	34	35	36	37	38	39	40
41	42	43	44	45	46	47	48	49	50
51	52	53	54	55	56	57	58	59	60
61	62	63	64	65	66	67	68	69	70
71	72	73	74	75	76	77	78	79	80
81	82	83	84	85	86	87	88	89	90
91	92	93	94	95	96	97	98	99	100

Guided Instruction Count to 100 by ones and tens.

Introduce the terms **count by ones, count by tens, rows**, and **columns**.

Count by ones. Trace the circle around the 1. Start at 1 and count aloud to 100.
Touch each number as you count across each row.
Count by tens. Trace the line under the 10. Start at 10 and count by tens.
Touch each number going down the column as you count.

1	2	3	4	5	6	7	8	9	10
11	12	13	14	15	16	17	18	19	20
21	22	23	24	25	26	27	28	29	30
31	32	33	34	35	36	37	38	39	40
41	42	43	44	45	46	47	48	49	50
51	52	53	54	55	56	57	58	59	60
61	62	63	64	65	66	67	68	69	70
71	72	73	74	75	76	77	78	79	80
81	82	83	84	85	86	87	88	89	90
91	92	93	94	95	96	97	98	99	100

♥ 44, 45, 46, _____, _____, 49, 50, _____

🦋 10, 20, _____, 40, _____, _____, 70, 80

🧸 63, _____, 65, 66, _____, _____, 69

Guided Instruction

♥ Start at 44. Count by ones. Fill in the missing numbers.
🦋 Count by tens. Fill in the missing numbers.
🧸 Start at 63. Count by ones. Fill in the missing numbers.

1	2	3	4	5	6	7	8	9	10
11	12	13	14	15	16	17		19	20
21		23	24	25	26		28	29	
	32	33	34	35	36	37	38		40
41	42	43	44	45	46		48	49	

26, _____, 28, _____, _____, 31, 32

8, _____, _____, 11, _____, 13, 14, _____

35, 36, _____, 38, _____, _____, 41

10, _____, _____, 40, _____

Guided Practice

♥ Count by ones. Start at 1. Fill in the missing numbers.
🦋 🧸 🦆 Say the first number. Count by ones. Fill in the missing numbers.
⭐ Say the first number. Count by tens. Fill in the missing numbers.

51	52	53	54	55		57	58	59	
61	62		64	65	66	67	68	69	70
	72	73	74	75	76	77		79	80
81	82	83			86	87	88	89	90
91	92	93	94	95	96	97	98		

72, _____, _____, 75, _____, 77, 78

95, _____, 97, 98, _____, _____

60, _____, _____, 90, _____

MP8

50, _____, _____, _____, _____

Guided Practice

♥ 🦋 🧸 Count by ones. Fill in the missing numbers.

🦆 Count by tens. Fill in the missing numbers.

⭐ Zach put his finger on the number 50 on a hundred chart. He counted backwards by tens. He wrote the numbers he said. Write his numbers.

178 Unit 3 ■ Focus on Number and Operations in Base Ten

11   12

13   14

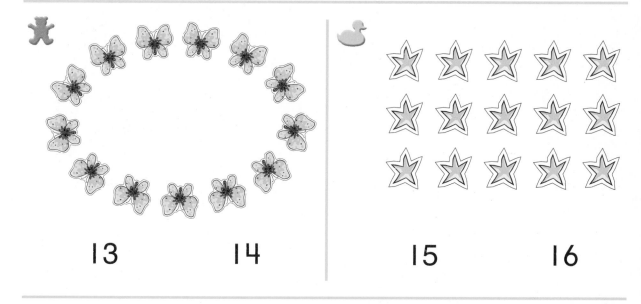

13   14   15   16

17   18

♥ 🦋 🐻 🦆 ⭐ Count the stickers. Circle the number that tells how many.

Unit 3 ■ Focus on Number and Operations in Base Ten   **179**

$$14 = 10 + \underline{\hspace{1cm}}$$

_____

_____

_____

♥ Count the flowers. Draw more to make 14. Write the number that tells how many more you drew to make 14.

🦋 🐻 🦆 Count how many flowers. Write the number that tells how many.

1	2	3	4	5		7	8		10
11		13	14		16	17		19	
	22	23		25		27	28		30

48, 49, _____, _____, 52, _____, 54, 55

80, _____, 82, 83, _____, _____

64, 65, _____, 67, _____, _____

93, _____, _____, 96, 97, _____

10, 20, _____, _____, 50, _____

♥ Count by ones. Start at 1. Fill in the missing numbers.
🦋 🧸 🦆 ⭐ Count by ones. Fill in the missing numbers.
🐢 Count by tens. Fill in the missing numbers.

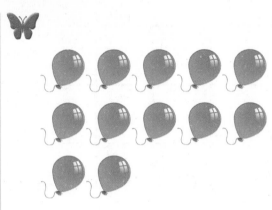

10 + _____ = _____   10 + _____ = _____

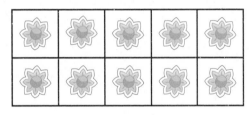

10 + _____ = _____

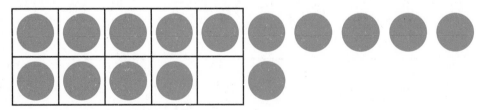

♥ 🦋 Circle 10 balloons. Write the number that tells how many more there are. Write the number that tells how many there are in all.

🧸 Count the sun stickers. Draw more to make 13. Write the number that tells how many more you drew. Write the number that tells how many in all.

🦆 Taylor has a ten frame with 9 counters. She gets 6 more. She says she has 16 counters. Is she right? Explain why or why not.

 **Progress Check**

In this unit you will learn about Measurement and Data. The lessons in this unit cover all the Common Core Standards for Measurement and Data.

To practice your skills, go to sadlierconnect.com.

Before Unit 4	Can I ?	After Unit 4
☐	**Talk about the length of objects** K.MD.1	☐
☐	**Compare the length of two objects** K.MD.2	☐
☐	**Talk about the weight of objects** K.MD.1	☐
☐	**Compare the weight of two objects** K.MD.2	☐
☐	**Sort objects into groups and count how many** K.MD.3	☐

HOME ◆ CONNECT...

In this unit your child will:

- Describe the length and weight of objects.

- Compare the lengths and/or weights of two objects.

- Count objects and sort into different groups.

Note: All of these learning goals for your child are based on the Grade K Common Core State Standards for Mathematics.

Ways to Help Your Child

Encourage your child to share what he or she is learning about measurement and sorting. Look for opportunities to involve your child in sorting groceries or laundry into categories. Discuss the height and/or weight of different objects. Ask questions such as, *How would you describe the length and the weight of the bicycle?*

Your child is learning to describe the attributes of length and weight so you may hear language such as *the branch is long, dad is tall, this book is heavy, your phone is light.* Listen for descriptions of how two objects compare as your child learns to use the terms *longer, shorter, lighter,* and *heavier.* As children interact with their world, they naturally classify objects: *This leaf is brown, this one is green.* They also begin to sort objects into categories, such as the leaves sorted here by color.

Activity: Gather objects of different weight such as food containers, cups, and books. Ask your child to choose two objects, hold one in each hand, and decide which object feels heavier and which feels lighter. Return those objects to the group, and continue to hold up objects and compare their weights.

ONLINE
For more Home Connect activities, continue online at sadlierconnect.com

Focus on Measurement and Data

Essential Question:
What can you measure?

Measurement and Data

Tall

Short

Long

Heavy

Light

 Which is heavier?

🦋 Which is taller?

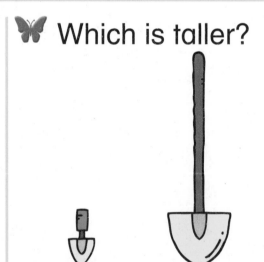

♥ Circle the object that is heavier.
🦋 Circle the object that is taller.

Lesson 39 Describe Measurements

Learn to describe measurements of objects.

K.MD.1

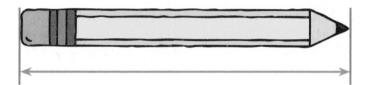

length

height

weight

Guided Instruction Describe how an object can be measured in different ways.

Introduce the words **length**, **height**, and **weight**.

 Look at the pencil's length to see how **long** it is.

 Look at the girl's height to see how **tall** she is.

 Hold the present to feel its weight and feel how **heavy** it is.

MATH

MILK

Spaghetti

P

Guided Instruction

♥ 🦋 Trace the ring around the line that measures height. Trace the X on the line that measures length. Tell another way you can measure the object.

🧸 🦆 ⭐ 🐢 Draw a ring around the line that measures height. Draw an X on the line that measures length. Tell another way you can measure the object.

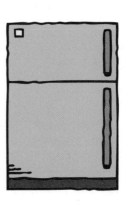

Guided Practice

 Trace the ring around the line that measures height.
Trace the X on the line that measures length.
Tell another way you can measure the object.

Draw a ring around the line that
measures height. Draw an X on the line
that measures length. Tell another way
you can measure the object.

MP4

Guided Practice

  Draw a green line to show how you could measure the height.
Draw a yellow line to show how you could measure length.

 Choose a classroom object. Draw it. Explain all the different ways
you can measure the object.

Compare Measurements

Learn to compare measurements.

K.MD.2

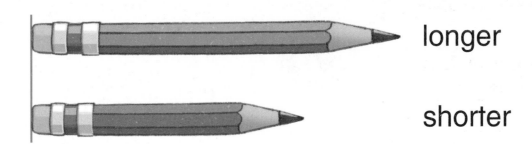

longer

shorter

taller   shorter

 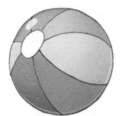

heavier   lighter

Guided Instruction **Compare measurements.**

Introduce the words **longer**, **shorter**, **taller**, **heavier**, and **lighter**.

♥ Compare the pencils. The red one is longer than the green one. The green one is shorter than the red one.

🦋 Compare the flowers. The red flower is taller than the yellow flower. The yellow flower is shorter than the red flower.

🧸 Compare the bowling ball and the beach ball. The bowling ball is heavier than the beach ball. The beach ball is lighter than the bowling ball.

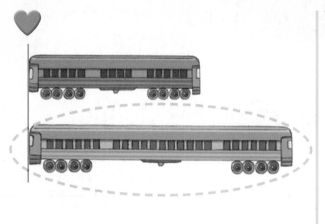

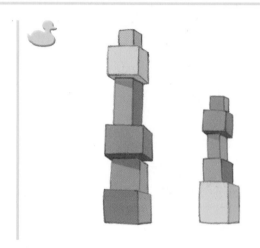

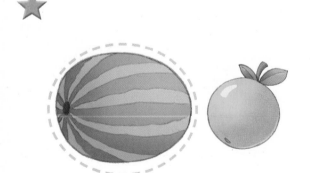

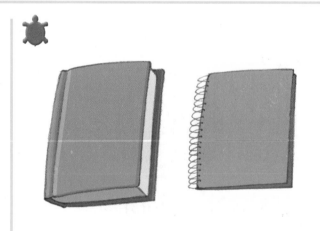

Guided Instruction

♥ Trace the ring around the longer train car.
Draw an X on the shorter one.

🦋 Draw a ring around the longer object.
Draw an X on the shorter one.

🧸 Trace the ring around the taller child.
Draw an X on the shorter one.

🦆 Draw a ring around the taller tower.
Draw an X on the shorter one.

⭐ Trace the ring around the heavier fruit.
Draw an X on the lighter one.

🐢 Draw a ring around the heavier book.
Draw an X on the lighter one.

♥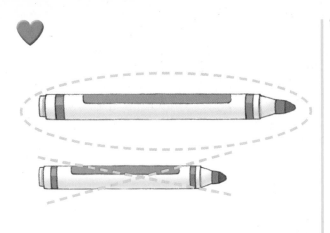

🦋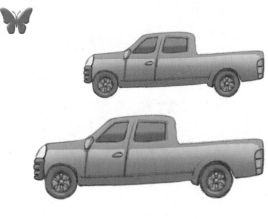

🐻

🦆

⭐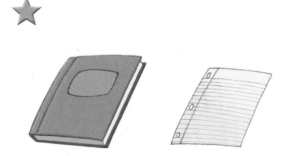

🐢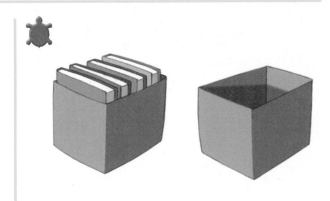

Guided Practice

♥ Trace the ring around the longer marker.
Trace the X on the shorter one.

🦋 Draw a ring around the longer truck.
Draw an X on the shorter one.

🐻 Draw a ring around the taller glass.
Draw an X on the shorter one.

🦆 Draw a ring around the taller doll.
Draw an X on the shorter one.

⭐ Draw a ring around the heavier object.
Draw an X on the lighter one.

🐢 Draw a ring around the heavier box.
Draw an X on the lighter one.

♥

🦋　　　　　　　　　　　　　🧸

　　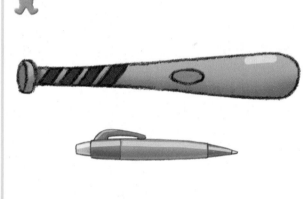

🦆
MP4

Guided Practice

♥ Draw a ring around the longer ribbon. Draw an X on the shorter one.

🦋 Draw a ring around the shorter flower. Draw an X on the taller one.

🧸 Draw a ring around the lighter object. Draw an X on the heavier one.

🦆 Draw an object that is shorter and heavier than the feather.

Learn to sort and count.

K.MD.3

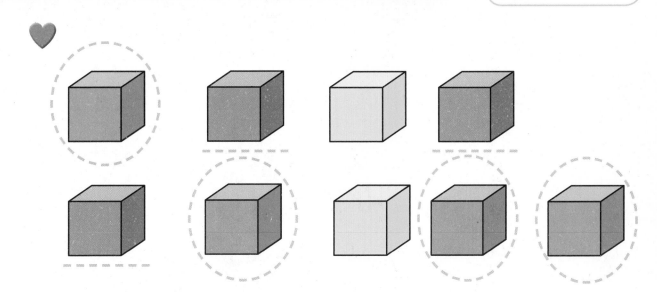

Guided Instruction   **Sort and count objects.**

♥ Trace the ring around each red cube. Trace the line under each blue cube. Draw an X on each yellow cube.

🦋 Count the red cubes you circled. Trace the number that tells how many.

🧸 Count the blue cubes you underlined. Write the number that tells how many.

🦆 Count the yellow cubes you drew an X on. Write the number that tells how many.

2

_ _ _ _ _ _ _ _ _ _ _ _

_ _ _ _ _ _ _ _ _ _ _ _

Guided Instruction

♥ Trace each circle that is around a bunny. Trace each line
   that is under a teddy bear. Draw an X on each dog.
🦋 Count the bunnies you circled. Trace the number that tells how many.
🧸 Count the teddy bears you underlined. Write the number that tells how many.
🦆 Count the dogs you put an X on. Write the number that tells how many.

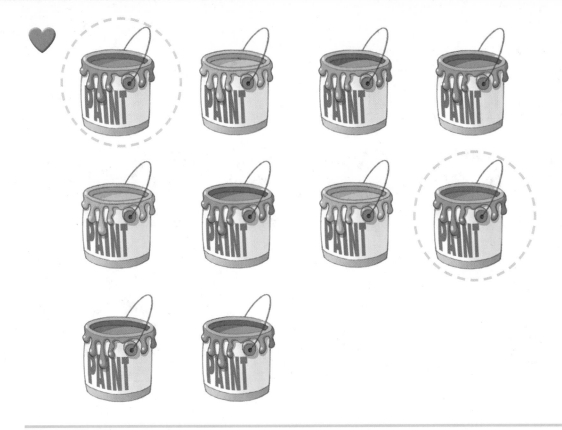

2

Guided Practice

♥ Trace the circle around each purple paint can. Draw a line under each orange paint can. Draw a line above each green paint can. Draw an X on each blue paint can.

🦋 Count the purple paint cans. Trace the number that tells how many.

🧸 Count the orange paint cans. Write the number that tells how many.

🦆 Count the green paint cans. Write the number that tells how many.

⭐ Count the blue paint cans. Write the number that tells how many.

Unit 4 ■ Focus on Measurement and Data   **197**

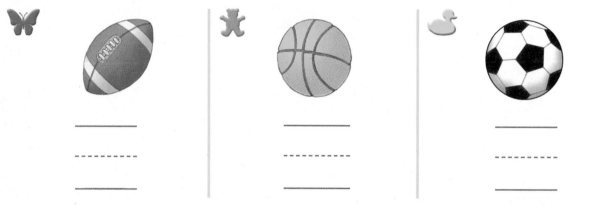

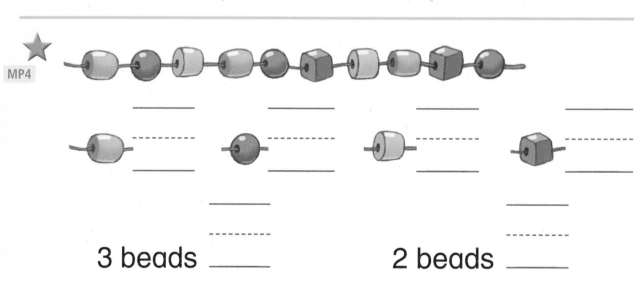

3 beads _____

2 beads _____

Guided Practice

♥ Draw a ring around each football. Draw a line under each basketball. Draw an X on each soccer ball.

🦋 Count the footballs you circled. Write the number that tells how many.

🧸 Count the basketballs you underlined. Write the number that tells how many.

🦆 Count the soccer balls you put an X on. Write the number that tells how many.

⭐ Count and write how many of each color bead. How many groups have 3 beads? Write the number. How many groups have 2 beads? Write the number.

198 **Unit 4** ■ Focus on Measurement and Data

♥ Draw a ring around the line that measures height. Draw an X on the line that measures length.

🦋 🧸 Draw a blue line to show how you could measure the length. Draw a red line to show how you could measure the height.

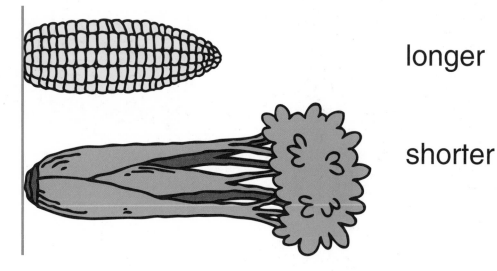

longer

shorter

 Draw a ring around the taller object. Draw an X on the shorter object.

 Which object is longer? Draw a line from that object to the word *longer*.
Which object is shorter? Draw a line from that object to the word *shorter*.

lighter

heavier

 _____ _____ _____ _____

♥ Which object is lighter? Draw a line from that object to the word *lighter*.
  Which object is heavier? Draw a line from that object to the word *heavier*.

🦋 Draw a ring around each orange. Draw a line under each apple.
  Draw an X on each pear.

🧸 Count the oranges you circled. Write the number. Count the apples you underlined.
  Write the number. Count the pears you put an X on. Write the number.

MP6

MP4

_ _ _ _ _ _ _ _

_ _ _ _ _ _ _ _

_ _ _ _ _ _ _ _

_ _ _ _ _ _ _ _

_____
- - - - - - -
groups of 2 _____

_____
- - - - - - -
groups of 1 _____

♥ Draw an object that is shorter and heavier than the container of milk.
🦋 Count and write how many of each animal. How many groups of 2 are there?
Write the number. How many groups of 1 are there? Write the number.

Progress Check

In this unit you will learn about Geometry. The lessons in this unit cover all the Common Core Standards for Geometry.

To practice your skills, go to sadlierconnect.com.

Unit **5**

Before Unit 5	Can I ?	After Unit 5
☐	Name the shape of objects: circles, triangles, squares, rectangles, and hexagons K.G.2	☐
☐	Compare shapes K.G.4	☐
☐	Name the shape of objects: cubes, cones, cylinders, and spheres K.G.2	☐
☐	Describe the position of objects K.G.1	☐
☐	Identify flat and solid shapes K.G.3	☐
☐	Model and draw shapes K.G.5	☐
☐	Build larger shapes K.G.6	☐

In this unit your child will:

- Identify and describe shapes in his or her environment.

- Analyze and compare shapes.

- Make shapes.

- Combine shapes to form larger shapes.

Note: All of these learning goals for your child are based on the Grade K Common Core State Standards for Mathematics.

Ways to Help Your Child

A young child's ability to understand the concepts may be enhanced by hands-on experiences. Some children grasp the attributes of shapes by using their fingers to create them in the sand or with finger paint. Solid shapes can be created with modeling clay or dough and explored through block building.

This year your child is learning to recognize and name two-dimensional shapes and three-dimensional shapes, as well as their position (*above*, *behind*, *below*, and so on). When describing a shape, your child uses terms like *sides*, *corners*, *flat*, and *solid* and begins to compare the shapes.

Learning to build and draw shapes, such as a triangle, requires an understanding of what makes up a triangle: three straight sides. Your child will also create shapes from smaller ones, such as shown here. Here 2 squares were put together to make a rectangle.

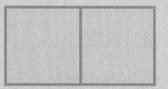

Activity: Tell your child to go on a shape search in the home. First ask him or her to predict the shapes that will be found. Expect discoveries of flat shapes such as circles and squares and solid shapes such as spheres (balls) and boxes (cubes), as well as cylinders (cans). You might ask your child to draw a picture of each shape as it is located.

ONLINE

For more Home Connect activities, continue online at sadlierconnect.com

Focus on Geometry

Essential Question:
What shapes do you see?

Geometry

circle

square

rectangle

triangle

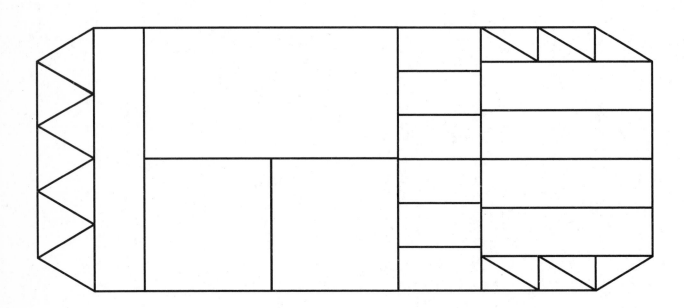

Name each shape.
Look at the shapes in the quilt.
Color the squares yellow.
Color the rectangles red.
Color the triangles blue.

Learn to identify circles and triangles.

K.G.2

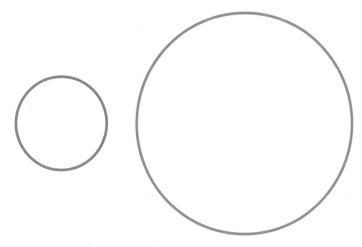

circle

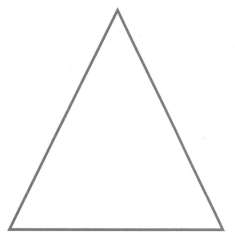

triangle

Guided Instruction **Identify triangles and circles.**

 Trace the shapes with your finger. Each one is a **circle**. Name something that is shaped like a circle.

 Trace the shapes with your finger. Each one is a **triangle**. Name something that is shaped like a triangle.

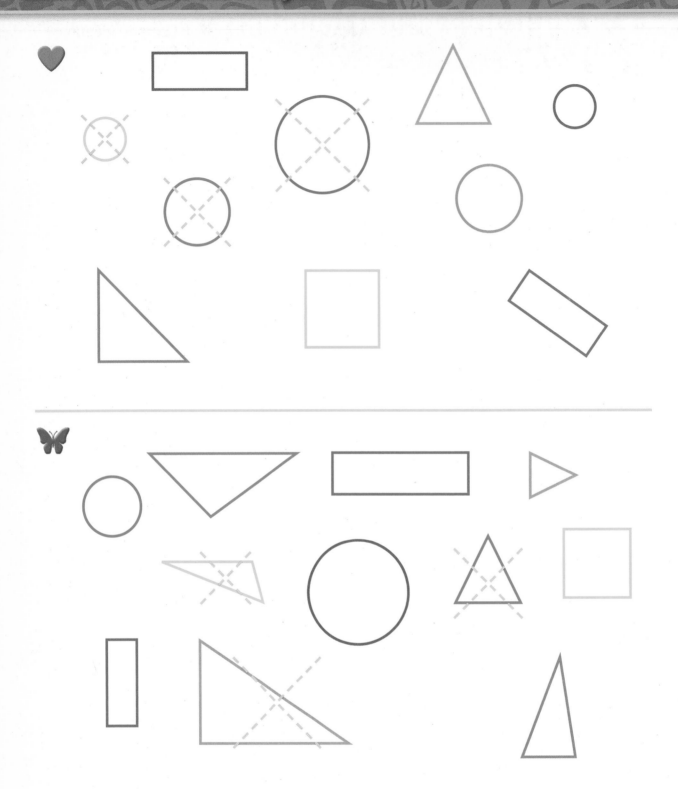

Guided Instruction

♥ Trace the Xs on the circles. Put Xs on other circles.
🦋 Trace the Xs on the triangles. Put Xs on other triangles.

Guided Practice

♥ Color the circles yellow. Color the triangles blue.

MP4

Guided Practice

♥ Color the circles orange. Color the triangles green.

🦋 Using these 3 circles, Sam made a picture of something you can build on a snowy winter day. Draw what you think he might have made using these circles. Add a triangle for a nose and a hat.

Learn to identify squares, rectangles, and hexagons.

K.G.2

square

 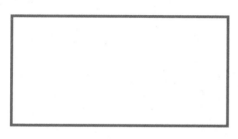 

rectangle

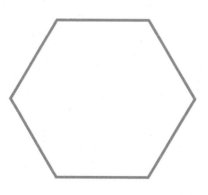 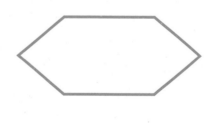

hexagon

Guided Instruction Identify squares, rectangles, and hexagons.

♥ Trace the shapes with your finger. Each one is a **square**. Name something that is shaped like a square.

🦋 Trace the shapes with your finger. Each one is a **rectangle**. Name something that is shaped like a rectangle.

🧸 Trace the shapes with your finger. Each one is a **hexagon**. Name something that is shaped like a hexagon.

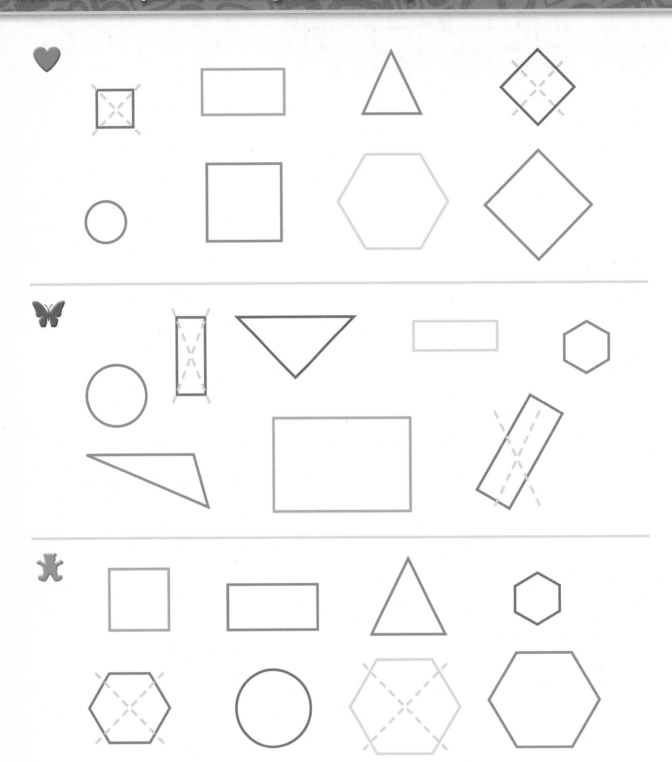

Guided Instruction

♥ Trace the Xs on the squares. Put Xs on the other squares.

🦋 Trace the Xs on the rectangles. Put Xs on the other rectangles.

🧸 Trace the Xs on the hexagons. Put Xs on the other hexagons.

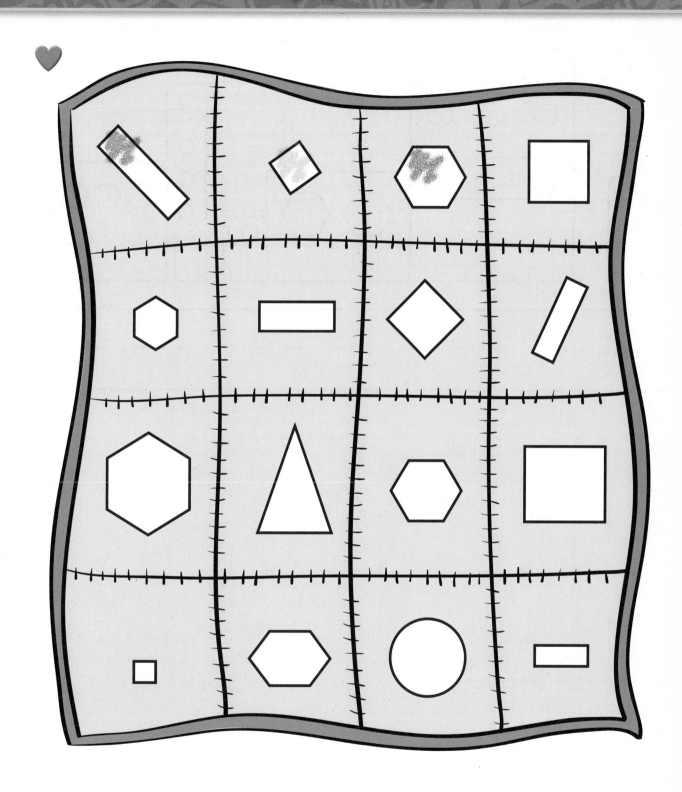

Guided Practice

💜 Color the squares yellow. Color the rectangles red.
Color the hexagons blue.

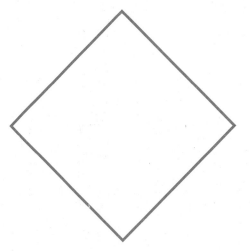

MP3

Guided Practice

♥ Trace the squares with a green crayon. Trace the rectangles with an orange crayon. Trace the hexagons with a purple crayon.

🦋 Shakira says both of these shapes are squares. Is she correct? Explain why or why not.

Learn to compare
flat shapes.

K.G.4

 side

corner

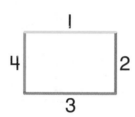

1
4   2
3

_____ sides

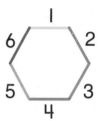

1
6   2
5   3
4

_____ sides

1
2   3

_____ corners

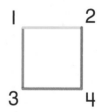

1   2
3   4

_____ corners

Guided Instruction **Compare and analyze flat shapes.**

 Trace the triangle with your finger. Each colored
straight line is called a **side**. Trace the rectangle
with your finger. Every place 2 sides meet is
called a **corner**. Trace the circle with your finger.
It has no sides or corners.

  Count the sides. Trace or write the number
that tells how many.

  Count the corners. Trace or write the number
that tells how many.

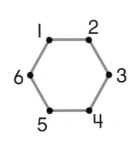

1

4   2

3

_____ sides

_____ sides

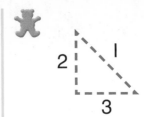

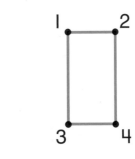

2   1

3

_____ sides

1   2

6   3

5   4

_____ corners

1   2

3   4

_____ corners

_____ sides

_____ corners

_____ sides

_____ corners

Guided Instruction

♥ Trace the lines as you count how many sides there are. Trace the number that tells how many.

🦋 How many sides are there? Trace the number.

🧸 Trace the lines as you count how many sides there are. Write the number that tells how many.

🦆 ⭐ How many corners are there? Trace or write the number that tells how many.

🐢 Count and write how many sides and corners each shape has. Tell how the shapes are alike. Tell how the shapes are different.

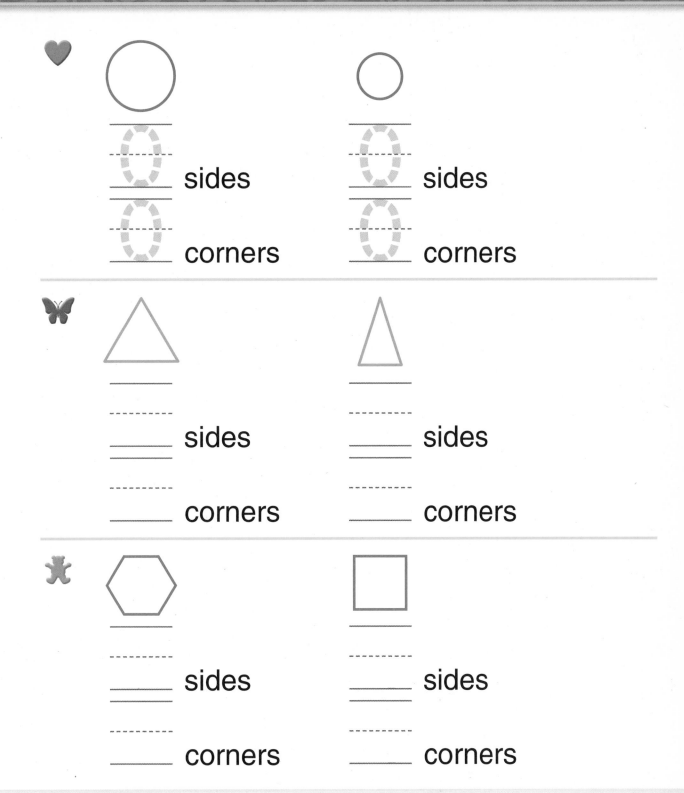

♥

____ sides

____ corners

____ sides

____ corners

🦋

____ sides

____ corners

____ sides

____ corners

🧸

____ sides

____ corners

____ sides

____ corners

Guided Practice

♥ Trace the number that tells how many sides and corners for each shape. Tell how the shapes are alike. Tell how the shapes are different.

🦋 🧸 Write the number that tells how many sides and corners for each shape. Tell how the shapes are alike. Tell how the shapes are different.

_____

_____ sides

_____ corners

_____

_____ sides

_____ corners

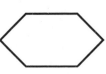

_____ sides

_____ corners

_____ sides

_____ corners

MP6

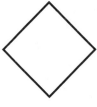

Guided Practice

♥ 🦋 Write the number that tells how many sides and corners for each shape. Tell how the shapes are alike. Tell how the shapes are different.

🧸 Color the shapes with 3 sides and 3 corners green, 4 sides and 4 corners yellow, and 6 sides and 6 corners red. Choose 2 shapes and tell how they are alike and how they are different.

Learn to name cubes, cones, cylinders, and spheres.

K.G.2

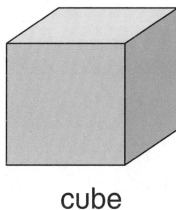

cube

cone

cylinder

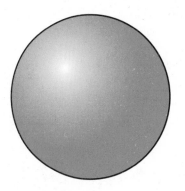

sphere

Guided Instruction **Name cubes, cones, cylinders, and spheres.**

❤ Look at the shape. It is a **cube**. Name something that is shaped like a cube.

🦋 Look at the shape. It is a **cone**. Name something that is shaped like a cone.

🧸 Look at the shape. It is a **cylinder**. Name something that is shaped like a cylinder.

🦆 Look at the shape. It is a **sphere**. Name something that is shaped like a sphere.

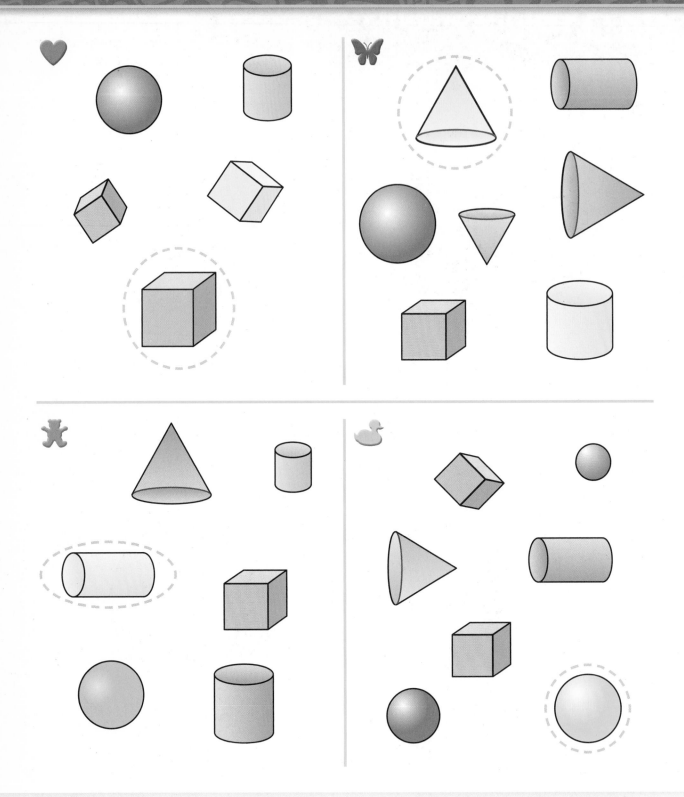

Guided Instruction

♥ Trace the dashed circle around the cube. Put Xs on the other cubes.

🦋 Trace the dashed circle around the cone. Put Xs on the other cones.

🧸 Trace the dashed ring around the cylinder. Put Xs on the other cylinders.

🦆 Trace the dashed circle around the sphere. Put Xs on the other spheres.

Lesson 45 Solid Shapes

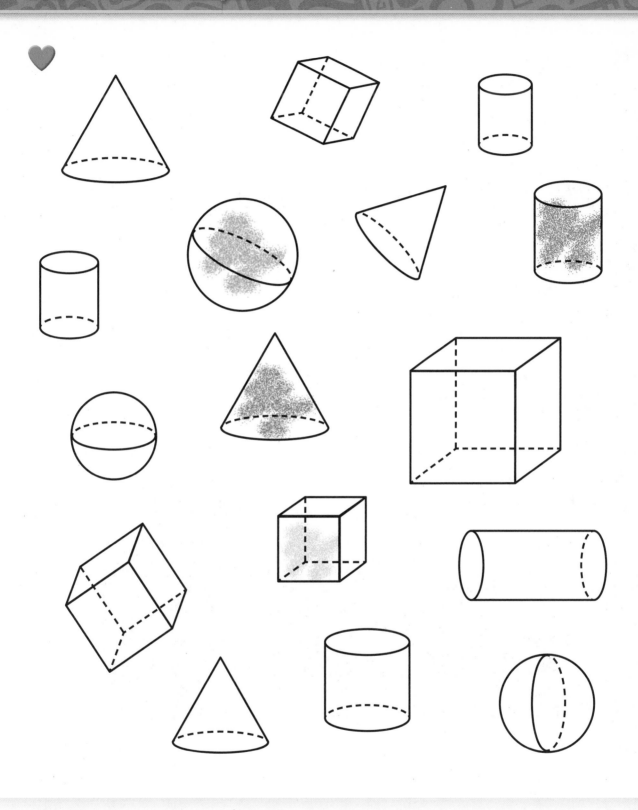

Guided Practice

Color the cubes yellow. Color the spheres orange.
Color the cones blue. Color the cylinders red.

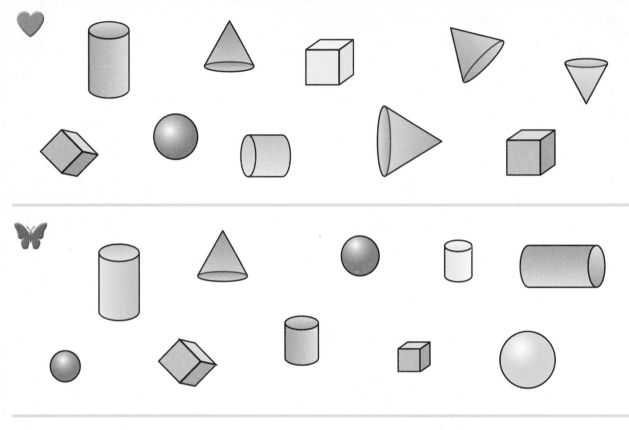

MP4

Guided Practice

♥ Circle all the cones. Put an X on all the cubes.

🦋 Circle all the cylinders. Put an X on all the spheres.

🐻 Use the words cube, cone, cylinder, and sphere to tell about the objects in this picture.

Compare Solid Shapes

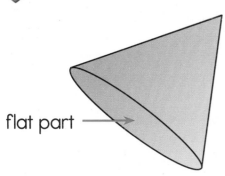

flat part

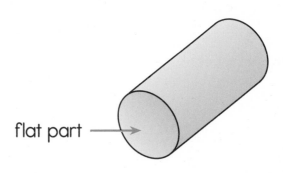

flat part

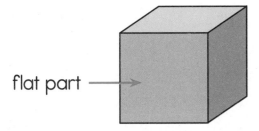

flat part

Guided Instruction Compare solid shapes.

Look at the shape. How many flat parts does it have? Trace the number.

 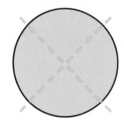 

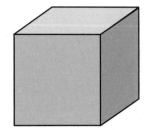 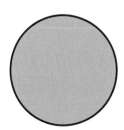 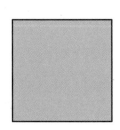

_____   _____

- - - - - - - - - -   - - - - - - - - - -

_____   _____

Guided Instruction

 Trace the flat part of the cylinder. What shape is it?
Trace the X on the shape that matches it.

 Trace the flat part of the cube. What shape is it?
Draw an X on the shape that matches it.

Write the numbers that tell how many flat parts
each shape has. Tell how the shapes are alike.
Tell how they are different.

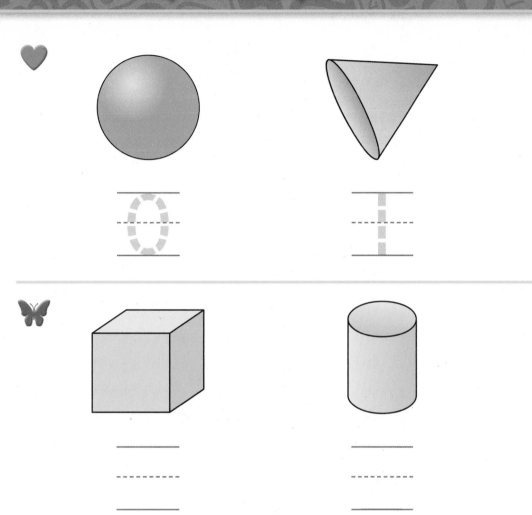

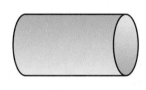

Guided Practice

 Trace the numbers that tell how many flat parts each shape has. Tell how the shapes are alike. Tell how they are different.

🦋 🧸 Write the numbers that tell how many flat parts each shape has. Tell how the shapes are alike. Tell how they are different.

♥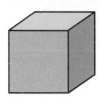

_____   _____

- - - - - - - - - - - -   - - - - - - - - - - - -

_____   _____

🦋

_____   _____

- - - - - - - - - - - -   - - - - - - - - - - - -

_____   _____

🧸

MP7

   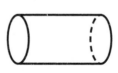

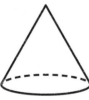   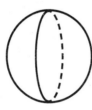   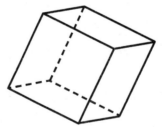   

Guided Practice

♥ 🦋 Write the numbers that tell how many flat parts each shape has. Tell how the shapes are alike. Tell how they are different.

🧸 Color the shapes with circle-shaped flat parts green, square-shaped flat parts red, and no flat parts orange. Choose 2 shapes and tell how they are alike and how they are different.

Identify Flat and Solid Shapes

Learn to identify shapes as flat or solid.

K.G.3

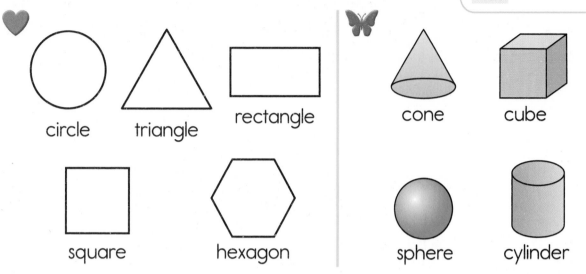

circle   triangle   rectangle

square   hexagon

cone   cube

sphere   cylinder

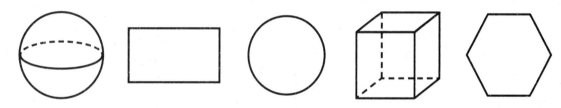

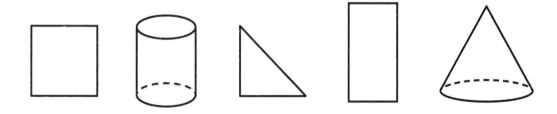

Guided Instruction Identify shapes as flat or solid.

♥ Name the flat shapes.
🦋 Name the solid shapes.
🧸 🦆 Color all the flat shapes.

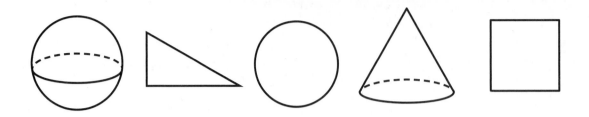

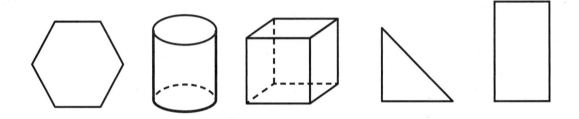

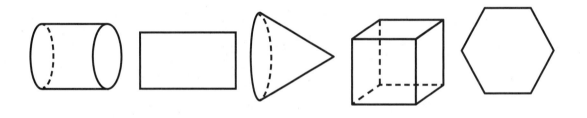

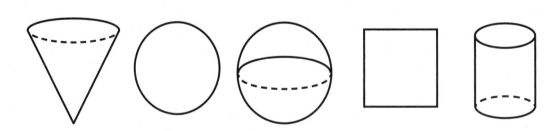

Guided Instruction

♥ 🦋 🧸 🦆 Color all the solid shapes.

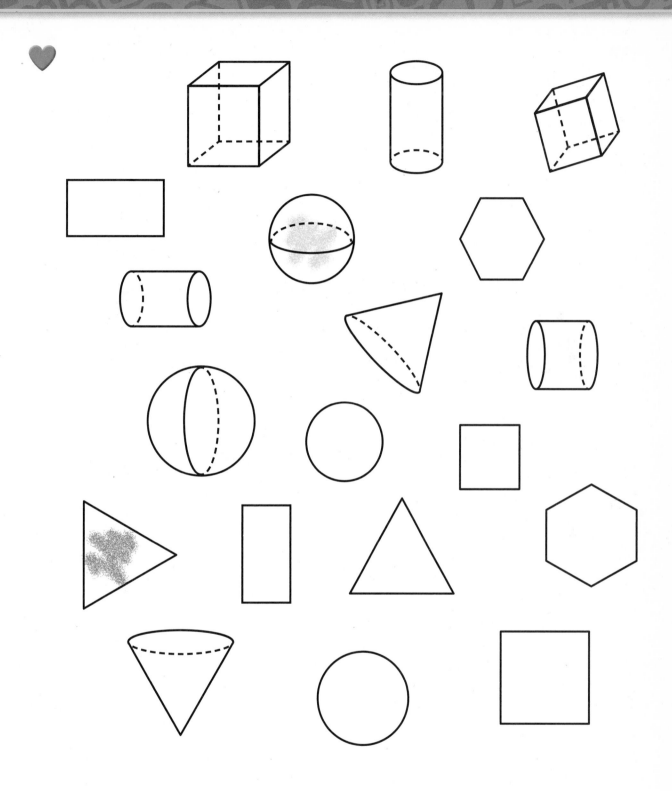

Guided Practice

Color the flat shapes red. Color the solid shapes yellow.

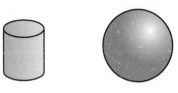

MP7

Guided Practice

♥ Circle the flat shapes. Draw an X on the solid shapes.

🦋 Look around the classroom for flat and solid shapes. Draw 1 flat shape and 1 solid shape you see.

Learn to use position words.

K.G.1

  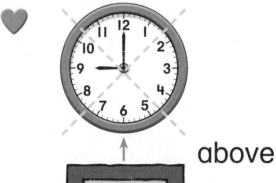  above

 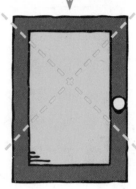 below

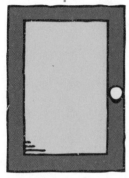  beside

   next to

---

Guided Instruction Use position words to describe objects using their shape names.

 Trace the X on the object shaped like a circle that is **above** the object shaped like a rectangle.

 Trace the X on the object shaped like a rectangle that is **below** the object shaped like a circle.

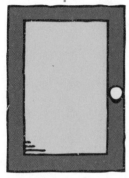 Trace the circle around the object shaped like a cone that is **beside** the object shaped like a cylinder.

 Draw a circle around the object shaped like a cylinder that is **next to** the object shaped like a cone.

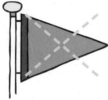

Guided Instruction

❤ Trace the X on the object shaped like a sphere that is above an object shaped like a cylinder.

🦋 Trace the X on the object shaped like a triangle that is below an object shaped like a rectangle.

🧸 Draw an X on the object shaped like a cube that is beside an object shaped like a cone.

🦆 Draw an X on the object shaped like a sphere that is next to an object shaped like a cylinder.

⭐ Draw an X on the object shaped like a sphere that is above an object shaped like a cylinder.

🐢 Draw an X on the object that is shaped like a cube that is below an object shaped like a cone.

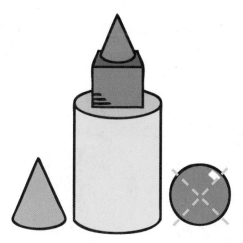

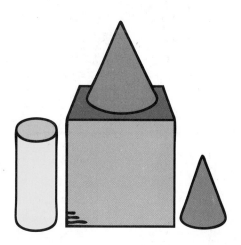

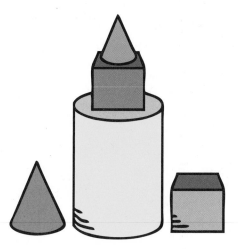

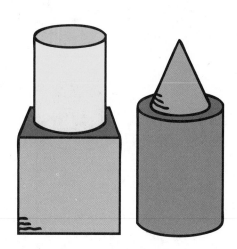

Guided Practice

 Trace the X on the block shaped like a sphere that is beside the block shaped like a cylinder.

 Draw an X on the block shaped like a cone that is next to the block shaped like a cube.

 Draw an X on the block shaped like a cone that is above a block shaped like a cube. Draw a circle around the block that is shaped like a cylinder that is below a block shaped like a cube.

 Draw an X on the block shaped like a cone that is beside a block shaped like a cylinder. Draw a circle around the block that is shaped like a cylinder that is next to the block shaped like a cube.

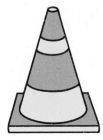 

 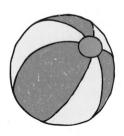    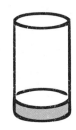

 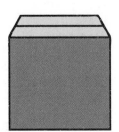 

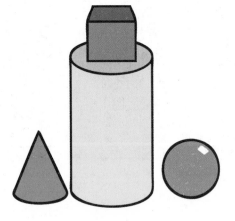

MP6

Guided Practice

♥ Circle the picture that has a sphere above a cone.
🦋 Circle the picture that has a cube above a cylinder.
🧸 Draw an X on the cone that is beside the sphere.

🦆 Draw an X on the sphere that is next to a cylinder.
⭐ Tell about the position of the cylinder 3 different ways.

49   In Front of, Behind

Learn to use position words.

K.G.1

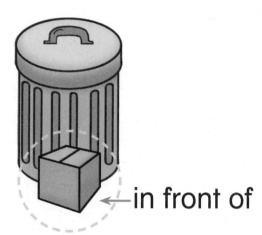

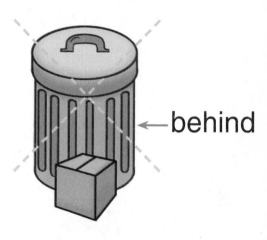
behind

in front of

Guided Instruction   **Use the terms in front of and behind to describe objects using their shape names.**

♥ Trace the circle around the object shaped like a cube that is **in front of** the object shaped like a cylinder.

🦋 Trace the X on the object shaped like a cylinder that is **behind** the object shaped like a cube.

🧸 Trace the circle around the object shaped like a cube that is in front of the object shaped like a sphere. Put an X on the object shaped like a cone that is behind the object shaped like a sphere.

🦆 Trace the circle around the object shaped like a cylinder that is in front of the object shaped like a sphere. Put an X on the object shaped like a cube that is behind the object shaped like a sphere.

Unit 5 ■ Focus on Geometry   **235**

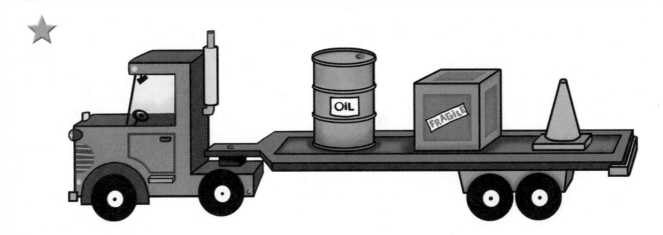

Guided Instruction

♥ Trace the circle around the object shaped like a cone that is in front of the object shaped like a sphere.

🦋 Trace the X on the object shaped like a cube that is behind the object shaped like a cylinder.

🧸 Circle the object shaped like a sphere that is in front of the object shaped like a cylinder.

🦆 Put an X on the object shaped like a cube that is behind the object shaped like a cone.

⭐ Circle the object shaped like a cylinder that is in front of the object shaped like a cube. Put an X the object shaped like a cube that is behind the object shaped like a cylinder.

236 Unit 5 ■ Focus on Geometry

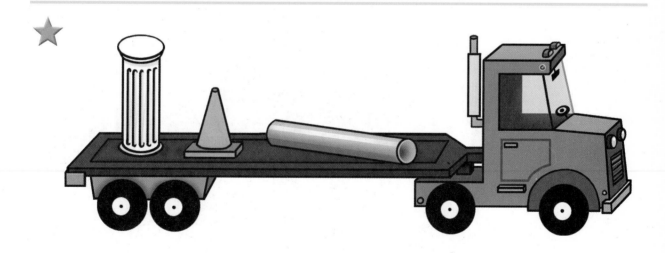

Guided Practice

♥ Trace the circle around the object shaped like a sphere that is in front of an object shaped like a cylinder.

🦋 Draw a circle around the object shaped like a cone that is in front of an object shaped like a cube.

🧸 Put an X on the object shaped like a sphere that is behind the object shaped like a cylinder.

🦆 Put an X on the block shaped like a cone that is behind the block shaped like a cube.

⭐ Circle the object shaped like a cylinder that is in front of the object shaped like a cone. Put an X on the object shaped like a cylinder that is behind the object shaped like a cone.

Unit 5 ■ Focus on Geometry **237**

MP6
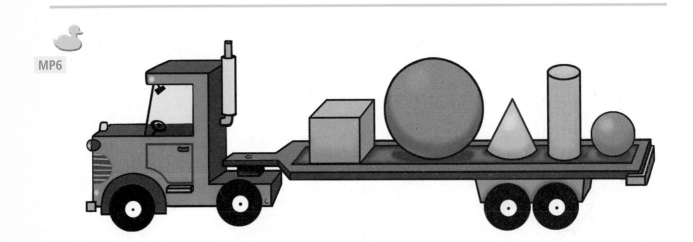

Guided Practice

♥ Circle the object that is shaped like a cylinder that is in front of an object that is shaped like a cylinder.

Ɯ Draw an X on the object that is shaped like a cone that is behind an object shaped like a cone.

Ӂ Draw an X on the object that is shaped like a sphere that is behind the object shaped like a cube.

🦆 Think of a shape. Describe the position of your shape using the words in front of or behind. Then let your partner take a turn to do the same thing.

50 Building Shapes

Learn to build shapes.

K.G.5

  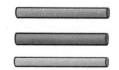 sides corners

Use

 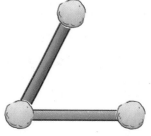

 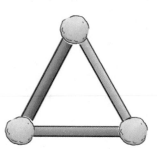

Guided Instruction Build shapes.

 Tell the name of the sign's shape. Trace the numbers that tell how many sides and how many corners.

Use straws and clay to make a triangle.

 Take a straw for one side. Put a ball of clay on each end of the straw for the corners.

 Attach another straw to make the second side. Put another ball of clay for another corner.

 Attach another straw to make the third side. Draw the shape you made.

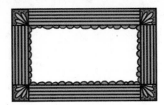

 sides  corners

Use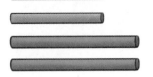

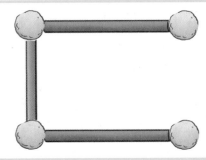

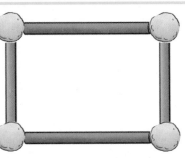

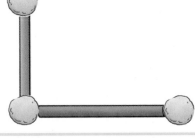

Guided Instruction

 Tell the name of the object's shape. Trace the numbers that tell how many sides and how many corners.

Use straws and clay to make a rectangle.

 Take a long straw for one side.
Put a ball of clay on each end of the straw for the corners.

 Attach a short straw to make the second side.
Put another ball of clay for another corner.

 Attach a long straw to make the third side.
Put another ball of clay for another corner.

 Attach a short straw to make the fourth side.

 Draw the shape you made.

 Use

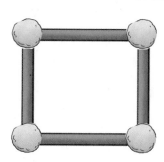
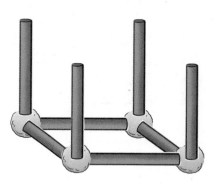

Guided Practice

♥ Tell the name of the object's shape.
Use straws and clay to make a cube.

🦋 Use 4 straws and 4 balls of clay to make 1 square.
Make another square the same way.

🧸 Put 4 straws coming up from one of the squares.

🦆 Attach the other square on top of the straws sticking up. Circle the final shape you made.

 _____ _____

_____ sides _____ corners

MP5

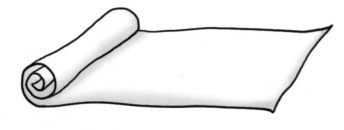

Guided Practice

♥ Tell the name of the object's shape. Write the numbers that tell how many sides and how many corners.

🦋 Make a hexagon. Use 6 straws and 6 balls of clay.

🧸 Make a cylinder with a sheet of paper and 2 flat circles of clay. Then use clay to make another shape. Draw your shape.

Building Larger Shapes

Learn to build larger shapes from smaller shapes.

K.G.6

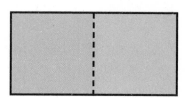

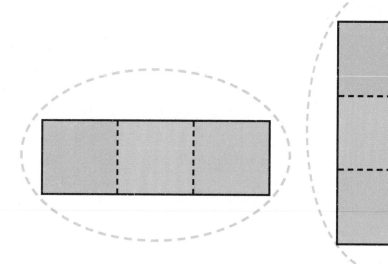

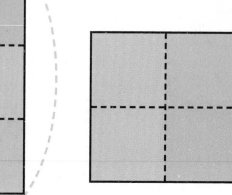

Guided Instruction **Build larger shapes from smaller ones.**

💜 Look at the 2 squares. When they are put together they make 1 rectangle.
Trace the rectangle with your finger.

🦋 Look at the 3 squares. When they are put together they make a larger shape.
Trace the ring around the shapes the 3 squares can make.
Name the shape you can make.

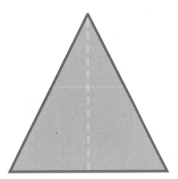

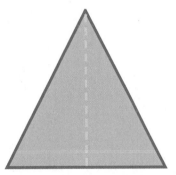

Guided Instruction **Have children look at the two triangles at the top of the page.**

💜 When the two triangles are put together they make a larger shape. Draw a circle around the shape the two triangles can make. Name the shape you can make. Trace the dashed lines to show the 2 triangles in each shape. Which picture shows 2 triangles put together to make a larger triangle? Draw a circle around it.

🦋 Trace the dashed lines to show the 2 triangles in each shape. Which picture shows 2 triangles put together to make a rectangle? Draw a circle around it.

 3

2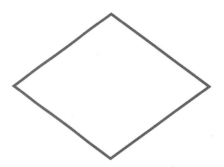

6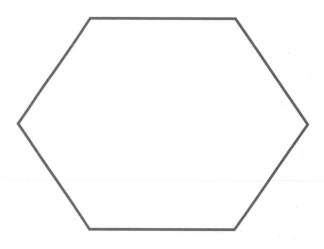

Guided Practice

Trace the lines to show how to make the shape with 3 triangles.
Draw a line to show how to make the shape with 2 triangles.
Draw lines to show how to make the shape with 6 triangles.

MP4

Guided Practice

 Draw a picture to show how you can put together 4 squares to make a larger square.

 Draw a picture to show how you can put together 4 squares to make a rectangle.

 Draw a picture to show how you can put together the square and triangle to make another shape.

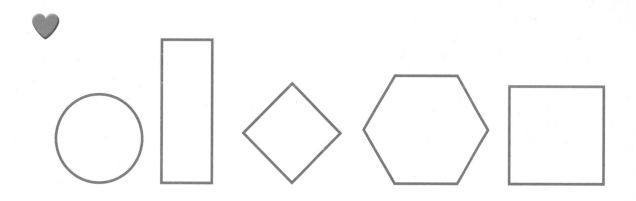

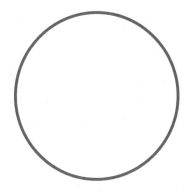

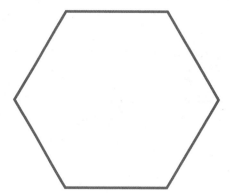

_____ sides   _____ sides

_____ corners   _____ corners

♥ Draw an X on the square that is next to the rectangle.
🦋 Write the number of sides and corners for each shape.
  Tell how the shapes are different.

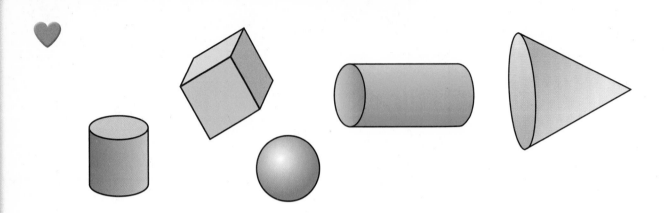

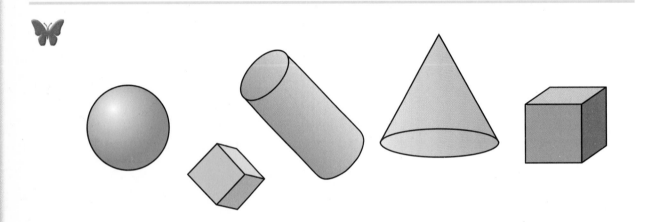

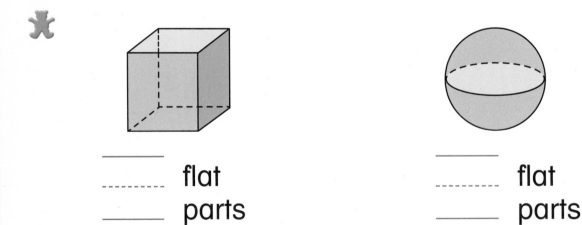

_____
_____ flat
parts

_____
_____ flat
parts

♥ Circle the cylinders. Underline the sphere.
🦋 Circle the cubes. Underline the cone.
🧸 Write the numbers that tell how many flat parts each shape has.
Tell how the shapes are same. Tell how they are different.

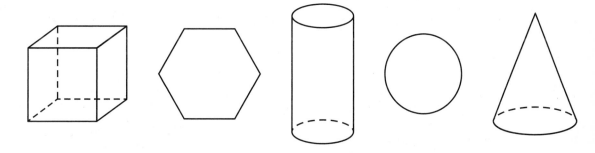

   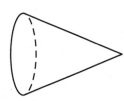 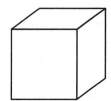

 Color all the flat shapes.

 Color all the solid shapes.

 Draw a picture to show how you can put together
2 rectangles to make a square.

MP5

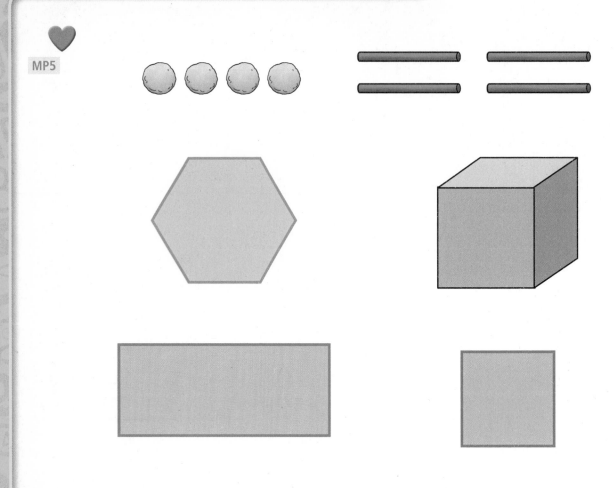

MP3

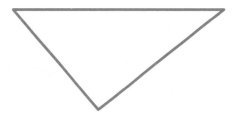

♥ Avery used these balls and straws to build a shape. Circle the shape that Avery built.

🦋 Matt says these shapes are both triangles. Is he right? Explain why or why not.

Performance Tasks

Performance Tasks show your understanding of the math that you have learned.

There is a Performance Task for each unit.

As you work, you will:

1. Show that you can use math skills.

2. Decide how to solve a problem.

3. Use different ways to model and solve real-world problems.

Tips to help you!

- Read each problem carefully.
- Plan how you will solve the problem.
- Check your work.
- Be ready to show your work or explain your thinking.

Counting and Cardinality

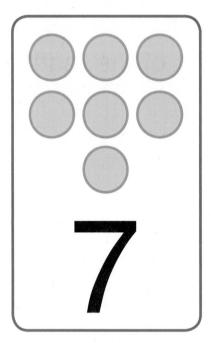

Show what you know about numbers to 10.

Ana and Trey play a number card game. Trey shows this number card.
Ana wants to show cards for numbers that are greater than Trey's number.
She wants her cards to show 10 or less. How many cards can Ana show?
Draw one of the cards.

Operations and Algebraic Thinking

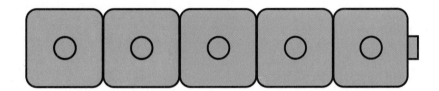

Show what you know about breaking apart 5.

Molly uses red and blue cubes to make a 5-cube train.
She wants to make trains to show the number 5 in all the possible ways.
What are the different 5-cube trains that Molly can make?
Show the ways with pictures or numbers.

Number and Operations in Base Ten

Erik shows you a handful of counters. He says that he has *ten ones and some more ones*.
He does not have more than 19 counters.
How many counters could Erik have? Write the number.
Use counters or draw a picture to show Erik's number.

Measurement and Data

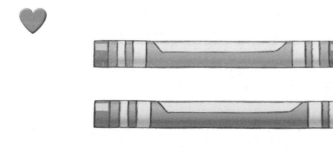

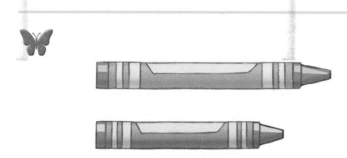

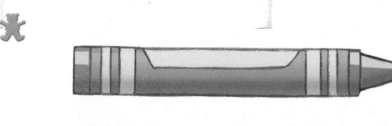

Show what you know about measuring and sorting.

The red crayons are yours. The green crayons are Owen's.

 Compare the length of the crayons.

        Draw a ring around the one that is longer.

        Draw an X on the one that is shorter.

        Who has the greater number of longer crayons, you or Owen?

Geometry

Show what you know about shapes and position.

Olivia needs to draw a picture of a shape with 4 corners above a shape with 6 sides. What should her picture look like? Draw it. Talk about your picture and explain why Olivia should draw hers this way.